From Fisher
to the Falklands

From Fisher to the Falklands

Vice Admiral Sir Louis Le Bailly

KBE, CB, OBE, DL, CEng, FInstMechE, FIMarE, FInstP

**Marine Management (Holdings) Ltd for
The Institute of Marine Engineers**

Published by Marine Management (Holdings) Ltd for
The Institute of Marine Engineers

76 Mark Lane
London
EC3R 7JN

British Library Cataloguing in Publication Data

> Le Bailly, Louis, *1915–*
> From Fisher to the Falklands
> I. Title
> 623.87

> ISBN 0–907206–40–9

Printed in the United Kingdom by Unwin Brothers Ltd, Surrey;
a member of the Martins Printing Group

Contents

Part 4   Stumbles and Triumphs on the Way Ahead

List of illustrations

The spirit of the Navy is too old, too varied and too subtle to be adequately interpreted by any outsider, no matter how keen his interest, how deep his affection...

We have been safe for so long and during all these generations have been free to follow our own devices, that we taxpayers as a body today are utterly ignorant on the facts and forces on which England depends for her existence...Some of us think the Navy does not matter one way or another; some honestly regard it as a brutish and bloodthirsty anachronism which if it can't be openly abolished, ought to be secretly crippled as soon as possible. Such views are not shocking or surprising. After generations of peace and party politics they are inevitable...

In peace the Navy exists under conditions which it takes years of training to understand; in war it will be subjected to mental and physical strain three days of which would make the mere sea-fight of Trafalgar a pleasant change. We have no data to guide us for the future, but in judging by our thousand year past we can believe and thank God for it, that whatever man may do, or neglect to do, the spirit of the Navy, which is man-made, but which no body of men can kill, will rise to meet and overcome every burden and every disability that may be imposed on it—from within or without.

Rudyard Kipling
An address to a Naval Club in 1908
Subsequently published in his *A Book of Words*

Foreword

by Vice Admiral Sir Robert Hill, KBE, FEng, FIMarE
Chief Naval Engineering Officer

Here is the larger book from which *The Man Around the Engine* was extracted as a taster. It traces the emergence of engineering into the mainstream of naval affairs. It is a book about people and politics: people who had a vision of the way technology must be understood and applied for the Royal Navy to develop as an effective force, and the politics of how they achieved their aims. As always, Sir Louis Le Bailly exudes enthusiasm for change, and relishes having helped to bring it about.

As a member of the first generation of naval engineer officers to benefit from the educational and career opportunities forged by the events the author describes, and in which he played an important part, and as one who has operated warship propulsion plants conceived by those whom he dubs 'the revolutionaries', I am very honoured to be asked to write the foreword.

This book emphasises Jacky Fisher's philosophy of an officer corps with some community of knowledge and a lifelong community of sentiment: a phrase which the author interprets in the present day context as meaning that all naval officers should be technically literate and a proportion should be professional engineers with sea experience. He sees the Royal Naval Engineering College, Manadon, as the instrument established by wise Boards of Admiralty, steeped in the lessons of the Second World War, to provide the engineering training essential to every category of naval officer, whose purpose also is to induce a common loyalty to the Royal Navy without any hint of the functional and social divisiveness which, in his view, was a basic cause of the fleet being sent to war in 1939 technologically out of date. The author suggests that this major policy decision, taken a quarter of a century earlier, was a crucial factor in the success achieved in the Falklands in 1982.

Many aspects of naval engineering today are explained by the event described in these pages. The central issue then was the mobility of the fleet; now it is the three Cs, *command, control and communications*. The field of technology is different but the same principle applies; to bring effective systems into service the Navy must itself possess people of ability, who are knowledgeable in the relevant technology and whose judgement is enlightened by the experience of having carried responsibility at sea for men and equipment.

The Royal Navy is indebted to Sir Louis Le Bailly for his powerful advocacy throughout a varied and highly successful career. We are thrilled that his voice now speaks from the pages of this remarkable book.

Preface

I described in the preface to *The Man Around the Engine* (Kenneth Mason) how a hotch potch of reminiscence and history I thought to call *From Fisher to the Falklands* came to be written: and how the publisher suggested that it should be carved into two parts. What follows therefore is the second part to which I have given the original title. Its theme stems from the report to Congress by Fleet Admiral King USN: the officer who held the highest naval post in the United States throughout most of World War II. He wrote,

> *'The Navy, perhaps more than any other of the services is dependent on a high quality of engineering skill and practice. All our ships and planes, the establishment which designs and builds them and the equipment which operates and arms them could not exist without the engineer and technical expert. Mobility is one of the prime military assets. The surface, submarine and air forces of the navy possess mobility in a high degree.'*

Thirty years later, General Sir David Fraser, who sat next to me at the Chiefs of Staff conference table and whose wisdom and occasional hilarious asides always comforted me when my credibility as deputy chief of defence staff (intelligence) was questioned by the great men at the far end, wrote in his brilliant book about the British army, *And We Shall Shock Them*, 'The Germans believed (and Guderian the father of the Panzer troops had ceaselessly taught) that they should regard the engine of a tank as a weapon, like a gun.'

Admiral of the Fleet Lord Fisher of Kilverstone who sought, in the first decade of this century by harnessing new technology to warship design and operation, to rouse the Navy from what Professor Marder has described as 'a moth eaten organism', would have agreed with King and Guderian.

Fisher believed that all officers should have *'some community of knowledge and a lifelong community of sentiment'*. In the context of his reforms I have taken this to mean that all officers should be technically literate and some of them, professionally trained sea experienced technologists. By the phrase 'a lifelong community of sentiment' Fisher clearly intended that the officer corps should be (in Drake's words used by the Mansergh committee in 1956) 'all of a company': a corps of different disciplines essential to the conduct of maritime war, but united by a common abiding loyalty to the Royal Navy.

In *From Fisher to the Falklands* I try to show that this is precisely what wise post World War II Boards of Admiralty, rejecting the views of their predecessors in the 1920s, sought and managed to achieve. Had they not done so the Falklands would now be Argentine territory: and we should not now possess a Navy which, though small, is probably, for its size, more militarily effective than that of any other nation.

Louis Le Bailly
St. Tudy, June 1991

Part 1 The Past 1882-1939

Chapter 1
The Profession of Arms

They left us a Kingdom none can take,
The Realm of the circling sea,
To be held by the rightful sons of Blake,
And the Rodneys yet to be.

Henry Newbolt

Apart from their very different traditions, any attempt to combine the three fighting services into one defence force would inevitably fail because of the different relationships within their professional structures whereby they manage their particular forms of violence.

In the Royal Air Force a multiplicity of engineers, with a wide range of skills, send an élite few into the air in highly sophisticated machines bristling with technologically advanced weapon systems and power units. Yet the pilots are quite alone as they fight the enemy and the elements. Their own lives and those of their crew are forfeit if they mishandle their instruments for a flash of time. A single error may well prove fatal.

This small minority must have faith in all their equipment and the majority who maintain it; for the odds against their own survival are far greater than those on the ground. Yet both groups are indispensable. The Royal Air Force has a short but already imperishable tradition; and, dependent as it is on the breakneck rush of technology, well understands that tradition is something to be lived up to and not on. In all this a thrusting aircraft industry and the challenge of space is a constant goad. Conscious of its glorious past, the Royal Air Force looks constantly to the future.

In the Army it is the regiment that counts. Drawn often from the same part of the country, the family remains an intimate unit through thick and thin, knowing each other's strengths and each other's frailties. The 'buddy' system, the tank crew, the section, the platoon, the battery, the company, the battalion, each man or group

1

is fortified by his duty to those he knows around him. 'Courage', Pascal said, 'is the only sentiment almost as contagious as fear.' Working together, playing together, fighting together, often suffering together and sometimes dying together, the Army rightly accepts tradition as a prop to courage, and so feeds on tradition and understands how to apply tradition.

For centuries the Royal Navy, with brief intermissions often coinciding with its triumphs, managed to perpetuate an always conservative and often very divisive tradition, by resolutely separating those who made the ship move from those who did the fighting. After a false start at the beginning of the twentieth century and a significant change of attitude in World War II in which the fleet air arm played a part, it is in fact only in the last three decades that a real change has occurred in this tradition; though there are still powerful elements of reaction. That the Royal Navy, despite such waverers, has now more or less achieved a 'new look', while still retaining the best of its old clothes, was amply demonstrated in the Falklands War, so perhaps the tale is worth telling.

Until Bleriot flew the English Channel or man touched down on the moon, the sea and, perhaps, the desert were the only places where mankind still lived on the borderline between what he could do and what the elements could do to him. Fundamental to the character of anyone who could live happily at sea or who aspired to leadership at sea, was the courage and ability confidently to confront the oceans of the world in all their savagery. The profession of seamanship remains one that demands great qualities of physical and moral courage and, when out of sight of land, intellectual qualities too.

Although brave men have roamed the sea far back into the mists of time landpower seems always to have been regarded as more important than seapower. Yet wealth was always the prize. Wealth could be dug from the ground and carried more easily by sea. Wealth could come from trade and barter with other countries beyond the seas and wealth could be captured on the way. In an always uncertain world, wealth meant more fighting equipment, greater security, and a better chance of national survival.

Seapower came to depend on traffic and the ability to traffic. Those who sought to bring wealth from overseas had to protect themselves from attack as well as from the vagaries of wind and weather, so fighting men had to be hired to guard the sailors. Some sort of mating had to be forged between those who made the ship go and and those who wielded the (land) weapons which protected them. History reveals that this was an alliance not easily consummated.

The antecedents of the British professional naval structure go back to the later Saxon kings, but until Admiral Sir John Fisher tried, eventually unsuccessfully, to change it and from then until 1956, when the Royal Navy at last realised how right he was, there was a fairly consistent and damaging anomaly. The soldiers or merchant venturers, under the sovereign's authority, dictated what the ships should do and carried out any associated military or privateering actions. The sea men, under the master, with the boatswain (the *batsuen* of Saxon days), the carpenter and the purser, despite their essential skills, were regarded as socially inferior, very much the servants, and were left to ensure that the ship floated, went where they were told to take it and was adequately provisioned.

Matters bumbled on until Cromwell and the Commonwealth government took power. Cromwell's 'new model' army is often referred to; his 'new model' navy less often. At that time there were plenty of sea men, but of the high-born accustomed to command there were practically none with a knowledge of the sea. So parliament turned to that magnificent and enduring pillar of the English scene, in those days just as in these, the army colonel. Their choice fell on Colonel Blake, who was at once promoted to 'General at sea'.

Admiral Hopwood, whose poems used to adorn gunroom bulkheads and who is still revered at the US naval academy at Annapolis, had this to say,

> '*On the anvil of their duty, Hawkyns, Frobisher and Drake,*
> *Forged traditions in the Service for the use of Robert Blake,*
> *Who adopted them in toto with the silence of his breed,*
> *And bequeathed to his successors, fully proved and guaranteed.*'

Unhappily one of those traditions, that of the division between the high-born who fought and who held the sovereign's commission on the one hand and those lesser mortals such as the master and his mates who made the ship move and kept it afloat, but were appointed only by warrant from the Admiralty, on the other, was nearly irreversible. When sail gave way to steam this arrangement came to appear immutable. That was not all. The antipathy to steam propulsion of all, excepting a few heretics, led to a distrust of all things technical and, in particular, to a contempt for its high priests, the newly arrived cuckoos in the nest, the naval engineers.

This contempt and distrust for new technology was not confined only to those who provided the new steam fleet with its mobility. Gunnery too greatly suffered. After daringly designing and actually fitting an embryo, but not at first very successful, 110 pounder breech loading gun, the Admiralty, instead of devoting resources to its improvement, quickly repented such a rash move and reverted once more to muzzle loaded cannon. Indeed twenty years later in 1882, HMS *Inflexible*, Fisher's first major command, still sported 16″ guns with a special deck house equipped with the hydraulic machinery needed to lift and insert the charge and shell down the muzzle. The industrial revolution, an unstoppable force, was meeting the nineteenth century Navy, at that time an immovable object.

As David Divine has written in *The Blunted Sword*,

> 'Of the twenty major technological developments between the first marine engine and the Polaris submarine, the Admiralty machine has discouraged, delayed, obstructed or positively rejected seventeen. The eventual and necessary incorporation of these developments in the structure of modernisation has been achieved by individual and sometimes undisciplined officers, by political or industrial pressures or—most frequently—by their successful adoption in rival navies.'

In most respects Divine's criticisms were well founded. The Boards of Admiralty in the mid 1920s, for reasons that will be explained later, set about reversing the measures designed to drag the Navy into the twentieth century that Fisher and Prince Louis of Battenberg had inaugurated two decades before. In particular, they refused to build on Battenberg's scheme for promotion from the lower deck and they abrogated the Selborne–Fisher schemes for a commonality of entry for officers and his arrangements for the education, training, equal authority and advancement, between the hitherto (military) executive and (civilian) mechanical engineering branches. Worst of all, they aborted at birth a seagoing electrical engineering branch, thereby setting back advanced weapon technology by many years, at great cost in lives and ships in World War II.

Chapter 2
The Fisher Reforms
1892–1915

*...the year (1902) witnessed an activity at the Admiralty which had
never before occurred in time of peace. Reform after reform...was
brought about by Sir John Fisher with bewildering rapidity. Engineer officers were to be given semi-executive titles; commissioned
rank was opened to the most deserving class of warrant officer; warrant rank was instituted for stokers through the new grade of
mechanician; an establishment for boy artificers was started...and
from this time onwards fighting efficiency* afloat became the main
object of every ship.*

**Previously 'spit and polish' had been the navy's constant pre-occupation.*

Sir Charles Walker
Private secretary to Admiral Sir John Fisher

Douglas Reeman, a well known author of naval fiction, whose research is always scrupulous, puts the following words into the
mouth of an Admiral in the 1850s. 'There is some small future for the
steam vessel, but not in any true sense as a fighting ship. Beyond
doubt, and entirely to my satisfaction, I believe the fleet in being will
remain under canvas and not be a victim of dirt and unreliability.'

Fisher's disturbing earthquakes had been bothering the many
conservative elements of the Navy since he became responsible for
materiel as Third Sea Lord and Controller in 1892. When he became
Second Sea Lord and Chief of Naval Personnel a decade later it was
as if a volcano was in eruption. It is helpful to the understanding of
what happened afterwards to describe briefly the origins and impact
of these groundwaves.

Captain Fisher first became known to the public when he put
together and personally commanded an armoured train during the
siege of Alexandria in 1882. He had also been witness to the gunnery
of the eight battleships (including his own) who, from anchor, had
scored only ten hits from three thousand rounds fired at the

HMS Inflexible, *commissioned in 1881 (photograph courtesy Imperial War Museum (IWM)).*

Egyptian fortress guns. Fisher was fortunate too that later the same year his ship HMS *Inflexible* was guardship when Queen Victoria visited Mentone on the Riviera. Thus he became known to her and, importantly, to the Prince of Wales, afterwards King Edward VII, who supported Fisher when his reforms later ran into trouble.

From HMS *Inflexible* Fisher was sent to the Gunnery School (HMS *Excellent*) at Portsmouth. The school had been mouldering on with smooth bore guns and elderly pensioners for many years and so Fisher was enabled to carry out a spring clean of dramatic proportions. Then he became director of naval ordnance (DNO), adding torpedoes to his responsibilities. He also took control of all naval guns and ammunition from the War Office, whose slothful ways had delayed the arming of new ships and who neglected to keep the Admiralty informed of ammunition reserves. From here he went for just a year as Admiral Superintendent of Portsmouth Dockyard. This appointment interested him in the operation of building warships and by concentrating workmen on one ship 'like a hive of bees' as he put it, he proved later that it was possible to build HMS *Dreadnought* in a year.

Vice Admiral Sir John Fisher, Commander in Chief Mediterranean Fleet, shortly before his promotion to full Admiral in 1901 (photograph courtesy IWM).

Thus Fisher was not without experience of the new technologies when he became Third Sea Lord and Controller. Further he had met and discussed engineering and scientific advance with men like Lord Kelvin FRS, Sir John Thompson OM FRS, Sir Charles Parsons, the inventor of the steam turbine and Dr (later Sir George) Beilby the great metallurgist. But it was probably Mr Yarrow (later Sir Alfred Yarrow, Bart), who set Fisher on the road to true mobility and better war fighting capability, by his wide knowledge of marine engineering and ship design. Through his international contacts Yarrow heard (and told Fisher) that the French were building some

Sir Alfred Yarrow, Bart, Founder and first Chairman of Yarrow & Co, shipbuilders, marine and power station engineers. Sir Alfred transported his budding shipbuilding company and the skilled workers by train from the Thames to Scotstoun on the Clyde in 1908. Since then his son, Sir Harold and grandson, Sir Eric, have continued to build warships for many countries. Sir Harold was responsible for the establishment of the Yarrow Admiralty Research Department (now a separate company, YARD). Although the Yarrow name remains, the Chairman of the shipbuilding company is now Sir Robert Easton CBE (photograph courtesy Yarrows).

exceptionally fast torpedo boats. In the pre-entente cordiale days this could not be tolerated and so Yarrow proposed to Fisher, who agreed, after consultation with his director of naval construction Sir William White, that Yarrows should build two prototype torpedo boat destroyers (TBDs). HMS *Havock* and HMS *Hornet* reached the then remarkable speeds of 26.1 and 27.3 knots respectively. *Hornet's* feat was important to both Yarrow and Fisher for she was fitted with Yarrow water tube boilers rather than the Belleville type which Fisher, against much opposition, had already introduced. (In a watertube boiler the water is inside the tubes and the fire outside. In locomotive type boilers fitted prior to the Belleville the fire passed through the tubes and the water was outside them.) The Yarrow boiler produced more steam for less coal and also proved more reliable than the Belleville type. Yarrow had also contracted to build for the Russians the *Sokol,* an even faster vessel due to the use of high tensile steel for the hull. This idea too, Fisher adopted and so, from Yarrows' ideas, the modern destroyer was born.

During his period as Controller it seems likely that Fisher began to realise that he alone, even with the help of a few equally forward looking but non-technically trained officers, could not possibly keep the whole Navy moving towards the benefits of accelerating technology. Such a task would never end and would need a band of

HMS *Hornet, first use of Yarrow water tube boiler (photograph courtesy Yarrows).*

*Imperial Russian Navy, 'Sokol', faster than the Yarrow TBDs due to use of high tensile
strength construction (photograph courtesy Yarrows).*

officers trained to a professional standard in engineering and able to
interpret the products of the industrial revolution and scientific
advance to those in the Admiralty charged with the shaping of
future fleets; and to facilitate this transfer of the new techniques and
expertise this new band of engineers must be seagoing so that they
fully understood not only the peculiar problems of war at sea but
also the problems arising from taking machinery, primarily
designed for use ashore, into the rough and salt laden climate of
ocean engineering. Equally non-engineers who had to conceive and
wield the naval weapon must be able to understand the language of
technology through which new ideas would be presented to them.
Fisher envisaged that there would be a drawing together of the two
groups and the highest naval posts might be held by officers from
either.

   After his tenure as Controller Fisher became C in C North
America and West Indies, but that appointment was cut short so that
he might become the naval delegate at the 1899 international peace
conference at The Hague. His early version of the modern deterrent
philosophy, namely that unless submarines were abolished it should
be agreed that their crews when captured should be boiled in oil was
not accepted. However, importantly, he realised from his meetings
with the German delegation that Germany's new fleet and

submarine arm would be complete and ready and anxious to give battle on their chosen ground, the North (German) Sea, by 1914. From then on every waking hour of Fisher's life as C in C Mediterranean, as Second Sea Lord, as First Sea Lord, as Churchill's unofficial adviser when the latter was First Lord, and again when Fisher relieved Prince Louis of Battenberg as First Sea Lord in 1914, was devoted to every aspect of fighting efficiency afloat.

From The Hague, Fisher went to command the Mediterranean fleet which gave him the opportunity to try out his ideas on those younger officers serving under him who were susceptible to his charm and vision. They became known as the 'Fishpond'. Once appointed Second Sea Lord he wasted not a moment. As he was to write to his daughter only four days after hauling down his flag in Malta, '...at 10 minutes to 12 I said how d'ye do to Lord Selborne. At 5 to 12 he gave me practically carte blanche, and at 12 I was read in at the Board, and 5 minutes after I commenced operations in my room in the Admiralty by sending the first pages to the printer of the preamble to the new schemes of training etc...'

It was these personnel plans to which Fisher had turned his mind since becoming Controller and on which depended his dreams of bringing new technology to the modernisation of the Navy's fighting power. His basic premise, that he would have to create a body of sea-going engineers with a higher academic and professional training than that of the current (but effectively very practical) engineering officers, has already been mentioned. This, he fully realised, meant that the latter's superlative craftsmanship would have to be replaced, so the boy artificer scheme was inaugurated. Young men of talent were recruited and given a four year training (initially and for many years) in marine engineering and a specialised craft, such as fitting and turning, boilermaking, coppersmithing and so on. This created a body of machinery maintainers who were given accelerated promotion to petty officer status and beyond as their operational experience at sea warranted; whose individual craft skills have probably never been surpassed; and whose exertions kept the British fleet at sea in both world wars for periods far longer than those for which it had been designed and under conditions more onerous than had ever been envisaged. The training was widened to include shipwright artificers and later to electrical and ordnance artificers; and from all four categories there was an avenue to warrant rank or, in exceptional cases, the Mate path (designed by Battenberg) to commissioned officer.

Concurrently a mechanician scheme was started which has been equally long lasting. Leading and petty officer stokers of outstanding ability were withdrawn from the fleet and after two years of (mainly) craft training added on to their already wide practical machinery experience, were given the same accelerated advancement and took their places alongside the artificers, with opportunities also to warrant and commissioned rank. Despite advances in sophistication in propulsion, electrical, electronic and weapon equipment and machinery, these highly qualified artificers and mechanicians still play the same and perhaps an even more important role in keeping a war ready Navy at sea, as Fisher envisaged they should nearly a century ago.

Fundamental to all these changes however was Fisher's determination to introduce a corps of engineer officers of a calibre that would command the respect of the civilian engineers and scientists masterminding the national technological revolution. In this, as in his quest for commissioned officers of all categories Fisher sought, without much initial success, to sweep aside the prevailing class distinctions. As he was to write to Lord Esher, '...this democratic country won't stand 99% at least of its naval officers being drawn from the 'upper ten'. It's amazing to me that anyone should persuade himself that an aristocratic service can be maintained in a democratic state.'

Such distinctions were particularly inimical to the profession of engineering. But in addition there were several other hurdles to be overcome if all Fisher's ideas were to be satisfied. These were

1. To open up all naval officer entry to the widest possible field and, once a candidate was accepted, to educate him at the country's expense. (*Author's note* Neither of these two aims were really achieved for another forty years.)

2. To establish a common entry for all officers including Royal Marines (though the latter idea was later dropped) between the ages of 12–13.

3. To give all entrants a secondary education slanted towards the technical and welded onto naval discipline. The two unhealthy hulks HMS *Britannia* and HMS *Hindustan*, then anchored in the River Dart would be scrapped and the cadets

educated first at Osborne and Dartmouth and then, when the buildings were completed, at Dartmouth only.

4. To abolish the separate entry of the (old type) engineers to the Royal Naval Engineering College at Keyham, Devonport and to reopen the College only when those of the new common entry opting to specialise in (E) (engineering) rather than (G) (gunnery) or (N) (navigation) or (T) (torpedoes) had, with their other contemporaries, achieved their Engine Room and Bridge Watchkeeping Certificates.

5. To reduce but not abolish the practical craftsmanship element of the curriculum at the RN Engineering College and inject more theory.

6. To improve the status of the old type engineers by substituting naval ranks such as Engineer Rear-Admiral for the old title of Chief Inspector of Machinery, with equivalent changes down the line. When Fisher became First Sea Lord in 1914 he insisted that all old type engineers should be permitted to wear the 'executive curl' on top of their stripes to show they were 'military'. But it was agreed that they should continue to wear purple between their stripes to differentiate them from the new (and as yet professionally untrained) (E) officers who did not.

The broad result (old type engineers apart) to be aimed at was to be, in Fisher's words, 'up to a certain point some community of knowledge and a lifelong community of sentiment'. It was Fisher's view that, when promoted to commander or beyond, all officers should be interchangeable, and for the (E) specialist this was a particular bait. Ships, squadrons, fleets, and the Board of Admiralty itself would, they believed, be within their sights.

In this aspiration Fisher was attempting to jump one hurdle too far, as he well recognised when he wrote,

> '...there will be immense opposition. There always is. Bows and arrows died hard in the navy, so did masts and sails; water tube boilers were going to boil our stokers! Salt beef has gone and the service is going to the devil, snuff boxes were made of it. Boarding pikes have only just left us. Greek is dead, but alas, Latin still lives as the shoregoing schoolmasters can't teach anything else and we must

have some test for boys entering the Navy; but they learn it no more after entering which gives Lord Goschen sleepless nights! The opposition was simply prodigious to Lord Kelvin's compass and sounding machine, perhaps the two most life saving of human inventions. A distinguished admiral, when First Sea Lord, objected to torpedoes because there were none when he came to sea, and the midshipmen having baths, because he never washed! Yes, the bow and arrow party are still with us and we are a 'retrograde admiralty'. They can't bear the Dreadnought. She is too fast and they hate big guns. They'll hate Heaven probably because there's no more sea and they won't like all the harps playing the same tune. Fancy! Complete interchangeability! Admiral Lambton and a Lieutenant (E) exchanging harps. It will be Hell!'

The discussion of interchangeability was not to be definitively resolved for half a century and indeed, even today, some would hold that it is likely to recur, at least in certain areas. The First Lord of the time, Lord Selborne was fairly well convinced by Fisher that officers from any specialist background should be interchangeable after reaching the rank of commander, but the Board, appreciating that the question would not arise in practice for thirty or more years remained sceptical. The memorandum issued on Christmas Day 1902, perhaps deliberately, was not entirely clear as to what future career the new (E) officers could aspire. And while offering considerable financial inducements to (E)s there was a caveat that choice would always be subject to the proviso that all branches would be satisfactorily filled. The crucial paragraph that left hope that (E) officers would eventually become interchangeable read,

'The ranks of engineer officers will be assimilated to the corresponding ranks of executive officers and the engineer officers will wear the same uniform and bear the same titles and rank e. g. sublieutenant (E), lieutenant (E), commander (E), captain (E), rear-admiral (E). The engineer branch will receive extra pay and although it is proposed to make the division into various branches definite and final, every endeavour will be made to provide those who enter the engineer branch with opportunities equal to those of the executive branch, including the same opportunity of rising to flag rank.'

It was this last phrase which gave firm hope of interchangeability. Traditionally (and the Navy has always been strong on tradition) a flag officer was one who 'flew his flag' in command of a

fleet or squadron; something no old type engineer had ever
envisaged. But to use the phrase 'flag rank' in connection with the
'new (E) scheme' was seen to imply that those specialising in (E)
might one day 'fly their flag', the phrase, 'to make the division into
various branches definite and final', being read as meaning that once
a (T) or (N) or (G) or (E) specialist there could be no swopping
between branches.

In a letter to *The Times* in January 1903, and later that year in the
House of Lords, Lord Selborne made plain his view and Fisher's that
many years must pass before the first (E) would become a
commander; and that it was only the feeling that it would be wrong
to tie the hands of a Board of Admiralty so far ahead that prevented
the making of a firm decision that executive and (E) officers would be
interchangeable in the higher ranks of the Navy. When Fisher was
First Sea Lord he had typed (in 1906) the following on a copy of the
1902 memorandum, 'It was the original and only sound basis to have
complete interchangeability, but in deference to a strongly
expressed desire not to fetter unduly, future Boards, the separation
into three branches was agreed to.' (*Author's note* The three branches
being executive, (E) and Royal Marine, although the latter scheme
was soon after abandoned).

The first few years of the twentieth century saw a great stirring in
the Navy. There was increased promotion from the lower deck,
although rather halting and slow, and more technical training for all
and better conditions of service for ratings. The (E) scheme for
officers was designed to bring the Navy fully into the technological
age. There was the steam turbine and water-tube boiler; nickel
chrome steel for armour; armour piercing shells (though as it turned
out not very effective ones); the diesel engine; better gunnery
controls; breech loading guns of 13.5" calibre; automatic quick firing
guns; torpedoes with greater range; aircraft; airships; submarines.
Behind most of these was Fisher's drive.

It was the combination of Winston Churchill as First Lord and
Fisher (by then no longer in office but still erupting with ideas), and
thanks to the extraordinary patience and understanding of Fisher's
two successors as First Sea Lords, Admiral Sir Francis Bridgeman
and Admiral Prince Louis of Battenberg, that created the biggest
operational eruption of all.

This started in 1909 when Fisher was still in office as First Sea
Lord and McKenna, not Churchill, was First Lord. Between them,

McKenna and Fisher conceived a building programme that would produce 12 battleships, each mounting ten 13.5″ breech loading guns each firing a 1400lb shell. Such was their answer to the German fleet now building and mounting only 12″ guns firing a 1000lb shell. When Churchill became First Lord he determined (with Fisher's encouragement from the side lines) to go one better and build a 15″ gun firing a 1,920lb shell. Churchill realised, under the tutelage of Sir Eustace Tennyson D'Eyncourt, his director of naval construction, and the engineer in chief, Engineer Vice Admiral Sir Henry Oram, that if such a gun could be produced two immense advantages would be forthcoming. Firstly four twin 15″ turrets could deliver a broadside of 8 × 1,920lb (a total of 15,360lb) and so more weighty than the 10 × 1,400lb (14,000lb) which could be delivered by the 13.5″ armament. More importantly, by sacrificing one turret, a battleship fitted with eight 15″ guns in four turrets would have more space available for machinery and therefore be able to achieve greater speed. It is of interest today that in the Fisher era a whole turret was sacrificed to give greater mobility in the form of speed. Forty years later the demand was for space to be sacrificed, by providing more efficient propulsion machinery, in order to permit more armament.

It is necessary here to turn for a moment from materiel matters to battle tactics. The only major warship battle since the introduction of steam had been that of Tsushima when a Japanese fleet, at peak serviceability and on its home ground, had destroyed a Russian fleet slowed down by bottom weed and machinery wear and tear from a voyage half round the world. The Japanese tactics had hardly differed at all from those in use in the days of sail. Then it was usual to gain the weather gauge and bear down on the enemy, either crossing the head of his line of battle (crossing his T) and thereby bringing the maximum firepower onto his leading ships or (as Nelson at Trafalgar) the same tactic but aimed at the middle of the enemy's line, which would create similar confusion (although with greater risk).

The steam equivalent of getting to windward of an enemy fleet was speed, and the loss of one turret by the substitution of eight 15″ guns for ten 13.5″ guns helped here by allowing more propulsion machinery. Churchill decided this was not enough and commissioned Fisher to chair a Royal Commission on Fuel and Engines. The aim was to assess the practicability of creating a fast division of 15″ gun battleships that could bring the German fleet to battle, while the slower ships of the British fleet caught up. The necessary margin of speed, Churchill was advised, could come only from the use of oil as a fuel, instead of coal. As a second aim, never realised, Churchill and Fisher still hankered after the Vickers design of a diesel engined funnelless battleship of enormous range; the precursor perhaps of the German 'pocket' battleships of World War II.

Royal Commissions worked fast in those days and soon Fisher was reporting the following advantages of oil over coal.

A shorter time to raise steam and an ability to change speed rapidly.

Oil fuel would give a 40% increase in radius of action over coal.

Oil fuel could be stowed in various compartments round the ship and pumped from there to the furnaces. There would be no need to use stokers (and sometimes guns' crews) to transfer coal from distant bunkers. The ability to pump oil about the ship would enable fuel to be used to correct heel or trim brought about by damage through enemy action. But the side protection afforded by coal bunkers would be lost.

Accommodation space would be saved because fewer stokers were needed with oil.

Oil fuel could be replenished at sea and underway. This would reinforce the fleet by the 25% normally coaling in harbour. (*Author's note* Although this was important as the fleet would have increased mobility the pause needed for coaling also permitted maintenance to be carried out.)

There were major problems too; all of them costly. To bring oil from a desert several thousand miles away would require a fleet of tankers. In addition, reserves of oil fuel would need to be kept available near all naval ports and bases, against the possibility of blockade or failure in re-supply, so a number of tank farms would have to be built and a proportion of the fuel would have to be kept underground (to be relatively invulnerable). Special tankers for fuelling at sea would be required and the warships themselves would have to be fitted for this difficult evolution. As Churchill summed it up, 'to commit the Navy irrevocably to oil was indeed to take arms against a sea of troubles'.

Assuming all this could be accomplished the Royal Commission entered one important caveat. Although the purchase by the government of a majority share holding in the Anglo-Persian Oil Co, at a cost of £2M, would secure a primary source of premium grade fuel oil, the Navy must, the Commission insisted, still be fitted with steam heating in ships and above ground storages for oils from other sources, which might have less pumpability under cold weather conditions than Persian oil.

Most of Fisher's reforms were in place before Admiral Prince Louis of Battenberg, who in 1914 had sent the fleet to its battle stations in Scapa Flow and elsewhere, was driven from office by the Northcliffe Press, to be relieved once more by Fisher. A fast division (the *Queen Elizabeths* with oil fuel and 15" guns) was building, but a boy who specialised in (E) after entering Osborne at age 12 in 1905 would not be likely to reach towards the top of the pole until the late 1940s or early 1950s. There was a lot of water to flow under the bridge meanwhile.

The entry of the old type engineer to the RN Engineering College ceased in 1910 as the first of the new (E) specialists (as yet untrained) joined the fleet. But it was the old type engineers, their morale raised by Fisher's insistence that they should be allowed to wear the executive curl and be regarded as military, who, by their skills and devoted loyalty to the Navy, carried the fleet through World War I. Many others, recalled from retirement or still serving, also played a critical part in World War II. Engineer Rear-Admiral Sir Henry Wildish was knighted for keeping the weather and battle damaged Western Approaches escort forces serviceable throughout the darkest days of the Battle of the Atlantic. Engineer-Captain Wilkinson, Cunningham's Fleet Engineer Officer, in the absence of the ship's chief engineer sick ashore, personally drove the Fleet Flagship at the Battle of Matapan faster than HMS *Warspite* had ever been driven before. The erstwhile Mr Mate Mill, by then a Commander (E) (and later a Rear-Admiral) was the first naval engineer to set foot in France on D–Day. Meanwhile, Engineer Vice Admiral Sir John Kingcome bestrode, like a Colossus, the whole worldwide engineering affair from Bath to Manus, the British Pacific Fleet's forward base.

For the young and enthusiastic (E) specialists with their Bridge and Engine Room Watchkeeping Certificates, the years just before 1914 were a time to live. They had seen their downtrodden and despised predecessors advanced in status as the crucial importance of engineering to the re-creation of the Navy's lost mobility and warfighting effectiveness was at long last recognised. Some of their executive counterparts still called them greasers, but such sobriquets they now accepted more with pride than anger. They were going to see to it that all the vast possibilities of the forward rush of technology would be used for the increased fighting effectiveness of the Royal Navy of which they now knew they were an integral part, for Admiral Fisher had told them so. War was in the air. Time was short.

Chapter 3
World War One and the Legacy of Nineteenth Century Drift

There seems to be something wrong with our bloody ships today—turn two points to starboard

Admiral Sir David Beatty at Jutland, altering course towards the enemy after three of his battle cruisers had blown up

There is something wrong with our ships—and something wrong with our system

Admiral Beatty to Rear-Admiral Chalmers, twenty four hours later

If Admiral Sir John Fisher and his fellow rebels had not been born the Royal Navy would have remained the rather primitive organisation they inherited. In that case the more numerous British fleet might well have been annihilated by the newly built German fleet, and an invasion or a total blockade and ultimate starvation would have occurred. As things turned out, a much improved, but very far from perfect British fleet was at anchor in Scapa Flow when war was declared in August 1914.

In HMS *Excellent*, the gunnery school, Fisher, helped by Admiral Sir Percy Scott, moved gunnery techniques forward from those little better than had existed at the time of the Armada. The divisions between engineers and seamen which he was later to do so much to negate were very evident in the later part of the nineteenth century. In any case, naval engineer officers were very practically trained with the aim of procuring and keeping the reciprocating machinery and coal fired boilers operational. They had no knowledge of gunnery problems, so Fisher and Scott had little advanced technological help in further improving naval gunnery. Fisher had only just started to make friends with great scientists and engineers to whom he turned for help with the wider problems of ship design.

Scott did a great deal, both at the gunnery school and later as Inspector of Target Practice, to improve accuracy despite the speeds and increasing ranges then becoming possible; while his concept of director firing whereby all guns could be layed and fired together by one officer stationed aloft, had been fitted to most of the battlefleet by Jutland.

Soon Fisher, as First Sea Lord, was largely instrumental in raising the speed of the fleet and the calibre and range of the main armament well beyond anything Scott had had to deal with only a few years before. These advances produced new problems of achieving accuracy just as the existing problems appeared to have been solved. The garrison artillery, using what was known as the Watkins system of fire control, was ahead of the Navy in some respects, although the land gunners did not have to contend with a moving platform or moving target.

In the Navy, two different avenues of advance were being explored. Lieutenant F C Dreyer, a gunnery officer with a brilliant brain was working with the Dumaresq and Vickers clocks. Fed with range from (not very accurate) rangefinders and human estimates of course and speed, the Dreyer table produced a moving paper plot (driven by bicycle power) giving rate of change of range. From this could be deduced the estimated position of the target as the shells reached the end of their trajectory. Dreyer relied partly on measurement and partly on estimation, and his system was preferred because some of the hardware was already available while the concept was unsophisticated and hence easier to grasp. If, happily, the salvo fell in line with the target, then the (garrison artillery) system of a 'ladder' of ranging shots (up or down) was fired under a well defined procedure which made the gun the rangefinder, so establishing the hitting range.

The alternative was a system devised by Arthur Hungerford Pollen, a barrister and business executive and later a journalist. The essence of Pollen's system was that his equipment could accurately calculate the enemy's course and, from these calculations, the aim for hitting, based on the minimum of possible human error was obtained. Such a sophisticated device was well ahead of the Dreyer system, but, with the exception of one Royal Marine colonel who understood Pollen's expertise, Pollen was categorised as a civilian outsider falsely claiming, against the views of the naval experts 'who knew all about war at sea', that his equipment would do the admittedly very difficult sums and transmit them automatically to the guns.

By 1906 Fisher was enthralled with Pollen's Argo clock and, in his letters of commendation to the First Lord arguing for financial support for Pollen, he implied that Jellicoe, then director of naval ordnance, was similarly attracted. However, Admiral Bacon, who succeeded Jellicoe as director of naval ordnance and carried on the pro-Dreyer anti-Pollen line, quotes the official view in rather less enthusiastic terms. 'The inventive ability of various other civilians was of value, and they received due recompense for their work and assistance.' Later Pollen went into journalism and annoyed Fisher and Jellicoe by publicly questioning Beatty's conduct of the Dogger Bank battle.

There seems little doubt that the Navy was looking after its own with considerable backing from Vickers and that the ship trials, with Pollen's prototype system, were heavily weighted against the Argo clock. Nevertheless, in the aftermath of World War I, it was Pollen rather than Dreyer who received the greater award for his invention. Not unexpectedly however, it was the Dreyer system that the Navy adopted.

It is easy to criticise naval gunnery, but even in World War II the rather new science of ballistics and of heavy gun design, the British quality control of shell production and gun manufacture, despite the

---

There is a vivid example of the problems of accurate gunfire between ships in World War II. On Boxing Day 1943, the one prolonged sea battle (discounting the Denmark Strait battle that sank HMS *Hood* and disabled HMS *Prince of Wales*, 24th May, 1941) with a major German ship (*Scharnhorst*) was fought through the twilight and dark of an Arctic day and night, in a full gale, with no intervention by airpower.

In the early part of the action, the two 6" cruisers scored direct hits and *Norfolk's* second 8" salvo caused a most damaging injury, destroying *Scharnhorst's* main radar range finder. After a long chase, *Duke of York* scored a near knockout blow on *Scharnhorst*, and, at the same time, *Scharnhorst* hit *Duke of York's* mast, severing the connection to her gunnery radar for forty minutes, just after *Duke of York's* 52nd broadside, at the extreme range of 21,400 yards, sent a shell which, due to the range and steep trajectory, at last penetrated *Scharnhorst's* deck armour into a boiler room. This instantly reduced her speed to 8 knots, rising to 22 knots after repairs. These speed reductions allowed *Duke of York* to catch up and close the range to 10,000 yards. With further, flatter trajectory broadsides she resumed destruction of *Scharnhorst's* turrets and fire control 'above decks', permitting the British destroyers to put four torpedoes into her hull. In all, *Duke of York's* ten 14" guns, at a range varying from 10,000 to 21,400 yards, scored 13 direct hits from over 52 broadsides, the first two, fairly low trajectory shots destroying one of *Scharnhorst's* turrets. Even after such terrible punishment, the strength of German warship building (previously shown in the destruction of the immobilised *Bismarck*) was such that *Scharnhorst* took a further seven torpedo hits (from 55 fired) before she sank, with 1750 casualties.

great advances in radar ranging, all militated against immediate and decisive hits on the enemy. To penetrate the thick tough German deck armour manufactured by Krupps, British shells had to hit at a steep angle, but such an angle could only be achieved from long range. And the longer the range the greater the possibility of ranging error

As Admiral Sir Frank Twiss, a gunnery officer and student of the Pollen system, wrote to the author, '...what, I often ponder is, would not history have been different in World War I had we had in 1905 a few qualified and bright engineers on the Staff or on the Board, instead of keeping them 'battened down' and out of sight'.

The trouble was that in those days naval training in engineering had hardly progressed beyond the practical. Clever men like Dreyer were not educated to take the products of Pollen's fertile mind, adapt them to the very real difficulties of war at sea and thus perhaps revolutionise the striking power of the Royal Navy of that era.

Warships are built to float, despite a degree of damage, to move and to fight. In the effective combining of these three essential capabilities lies the art of the naval constructor. Fisher, when Controller, had the services of a great constructor, Sir William White, but not even White or White's successor, Sir Eustace Tennyson D'Eyncourt, could ever design and build the perfect warship. Compromises and unsupported judgements founded on past experience, of which with steam driven ironclads there was little, were as essential then as now, but with the competing claims of hull sub-division (to minimise flooding from underwater damage), the size of machinery spaces (to give speed and mobility), weight of armour (to protect machinery and magazines), magazine space (to permit enough cordite and shells to be carried), guns (and turrets to protect them), living spaces for the crew and, most critically, the size of available dry docks for repair and maintenance, the best compromise was always a matter of fallible human judgement.

To attain the worldwide mobility that sail had conferred on the Royal Navy, the needs of steam ships and the defence of a growing empire created a global chain of coaling stations, some of which became bases needing army garrisons and a fleet of colliers to supply them with the best welsh steam coal. This worldwide responsibility also maintained the tradition that crews of British warships should be able to live on board for long periods as they always had in the days of sail. So a reasonable degree of habitability was another major design requirement. Although sometimes denied today, it has always been held that German designers were never so constrained by the habitability requirement as their British counterparts, because so much of the Kaiser's fleet was built with the North (German) Sea in mind as its battleground. It was in the North Sea that both nations believed their respective mastodons would fight it out; and each, certain of success, believed that its own side would win this modern Trafalgar.

Ship actions in both world wars, the *Seydlitz* and the *Derfflinger* at Jutland, and the *Bismarck* and *Scharnhorst* in World War II, have confirmed that the Germans have always designed and built their warships as mini-fortresses with plenty of high quality armour and maximum sub-division. If it was uncomfortable when at sea then, submarines apart, in World War I (and to some extent also in World War II) periods lying alongside the jetty in Kiel or Wilhelmshaven provided the crew with opportunities for shore leave. Fuelling with coal (as in World War I) or oil could be carried out from trains with cranes and civilian workers, or by simple pipe lines without tankers. In the British fleet in World War I after endless sorties seeking the enemy, there was always the terrible labour of immediately coaling ship on return to harbour.

In 1914, both fleets had similar machinery problems. The tube ends of watertube boilers were apt to leak at what were called the 'wrapper plates' around the water drums; and this came to be known as 'wrapperitis'. It led to a constant wastage of boiler feed water. Similarly the joints surrounding the tubes, through which seawater to condense the steam, after it had done its work in the main engines, was circulated were also apt to leak (condenseritis); and this gave rise to contamination of the boiler feed water with salt. (In *The Man Around the Engine* I recounted how HMS *Hood* was nearly brought to a stop on 26th September 1939, in the presence of the enemy, by shock damage from a bomb causing acute condenseritis.) At the best, if permitted to continue, such salt contamination would damage the boilers; at the worst 'priming', the passage of water droplets in the steam, would cause damage to steam joints leading to further loss of boiler feed water and sometimes explosions in steam valves, with fatal results to those nearby. In either case the only remedy was to ditch the contaminated water which would somehow have to be replaced by evaporating machinery or the provision of a water boat or some other conveyance with distilled water. In coping with these recurrent problems the German fleet, alongside or at a buoy in a safe harbour, could far more easily be maintained; while importantly, distilled water for the boilers and drinking water for the crew did not have to be made on board but could be supplied from ashore. German fleet sorties to lure the British fleet into a submarine trap or to bombard the east coast of England would be ordered only when the High Seas fleet was at the peak of materiel availability. At Scapa Flow in the Grand fleet, besides the constant sweeps searching for the enemy, it was often necessary to keep up steam in harbour or move engines to prevent the anchors dragging in winter storms, so preventing any but minor machinery upkeep. Thus for purely engineering reasons the German High Seas fleet always held the initiative.

British constructors also had to work to narrower beamed ships, arising from the need to fit them into the smaller dry docks built for an earlier and smaller generation of warships. Not enough money was sanctioned to build larger docks in addition to the number of warships planned. In order to maintain even the minimal stability this lack of beam restricted the weight of top hamper including the weight of deck armour. To summarize:

1. The German fleet had the initiative and could sortie when at a high state of materiel readiness. The British fleet, though larger and therefore with more built in ship redundancy, had a more difficult maintenance task.

2. British crews had to live on board and spent more time at sea. German crews lived nearer 'the bright lights' and their ships did not go to sea so much, so maintenance workload was less. However, German crews were more liable to subversion by agitators.

3. The German fleet was newly built with docks to match, so ships possessed greater beam, more stability and greater resistance to battle damage.

4. British armour and armour piercing shells were not well manufactured. So German shells were more likely to penetrate British armour and British shells more apt to break up before penetration.

5. German rangefinders were far superior to those in use in the British fleet and therefore German gunnery was more likely to hit earlier.

In his *Life of Earl Beatty* (Jarrolds), Geoffrey Rawson quotes Sir George Thurston the distinguished engineer writing in Brassey's Naval Annual, 1921 as follows.

'*1. The British ships were one and all deficient in underwater protection.*
2. Their internal subdivision was not carried out to the fullest possible extent.
3. The armoured side protection was too weak.
4. The deck protection was entirely inadequate.
5. The stowage of ammunition could have been improved.
6. No adequate provision existed for righting heel or trim.
7. The secondary armament was insufficiently protected.
8. The night sighting was bad.
9. The searchlights were inferior to those of the enemy.
10.The range finding was capable of improvement.'

Luck too was against the British. In the Dogger Bank battle Beatty, due to poor communications, just missed a considerable victory although his flagship was badly damaged, but the Germans learnt a lesson denied the British. A British shell exploding in the gunhouse of a German turret caused a flash down the turret 'stalk' towards the magazine, producing a considerable explosion. German sub-division and other precautions saved the ship. Immediately on return to Germany, design alterations to prevent a similar happening were implemented. In British ships, although HMS *Lion*, Beatty's flagship, was saved from blowing up from the same design defect only by the gallantry of a fatally wounded Royal Marine officer*, the risk had not been recognised; only to be revealed at Jutland at the terrible cost of three battle cruisers totally destroyed with the loss of most of their crews, due either to this design fault or to too thin deck armour.

Though Jutland was a strategic success because the German fleet hardly ventured forth again and the British fleet kept the sea, in the

---

*At the age of four, the author while being shown around HMS *Lion* by an Able Seaman, was shown the magazine flooding valves operated on the orders of the fatally wounded Major F J W Harvey RMLI (awarded a posthumous VC), thereby saving the ship, but drowning the magazine crew.

British battle cruiser HMS Lion *being hit on Q turret, Jutland, 31st May 1916
(photograph courtesy IWM).*

public eye, due to ship losses, casualties and poor publicity, it
appeared a disaster, and certainly no Trafalgar. The earlier loss of the
old cruisers *Hogue, Aboukir,* and *Cressy* in one hour, torpedoed by
Otto Weddigen's U9 and, later, *Hawke* and the battleship *Audacious*
in the first three months of the war; the escape of the *Goeben* and
Breslau to Constantinople; the bombardment of Felixstowe,
Hartlepool, Whitby and Scarborough with 500 civilian casualties;
the missed chances in the Dogger Bank battle; the disaster at
Coronel; the sight of powerful German forces in the Straits of Dover;
the failure to force the Dardanelles; all these, together it must be said
with the encouragement of the Northcliffe Press, despite the sinking
of Von Spee's squadron off the Falkland Islands and the rather
bungled battle of the Heligoland Bight, caused a change in the public
mood vis a vis the Navy. There was worse to come.

For the Engineering Branch of the Royal Navy however, Jutland
produced a commendation all too rare in those days. I was shown
para 31 of Jellicoe's dispatch not, as might be expected, at Dartmouth
or Keyham, but on an engraved plaque behind the desk of Admiral
Hyman G Rickover USN, the father of the United States nuclear fleet,

on whom I was calling, and by whom (I was told) I was being greatly honoured by being awarded a chocolate biscuit with my coffee. It read,

> *'It must never be forgotten however that the prelude to action is the work of the engine room department and that during action the officers and men of that department perform their most important duties without the incentive which the knowledge of the course of the action gives to those on the upper deck. The qualities of discipline and endurance are taxed to the utmost under these conditions, and they were, as always, most fully maintained throughout the operations under review. Many ships attained speeds that had never before been reached, thus showing very clearly their high state of steaming efficiency. Failures in material were conspicuous by their absence, and many instances are reported of magnificent work on the part of engine room departments of injured ships.'*

As the Germans saw it the existence of the British fleet and the ability of its engineers constantly to keep it battleworthy in the difficult conditions of Scapa Flow enabled Germany to be blockaded and starved. They could see only one answer, unrestricted submarine warfare, and they calculated that if this should bring America into the war on the side of the allies, Britain could still be forced to surrender before the American reinforcements for the Western Front could be recruited, trained and shipped safely to France.

Jellicoe, already a tired man, was succeeded by Beatty in the Grand Fleet and appointed First Sea Lord 'in order to lend his great experience', or so it was confidently thought, to overcoming the submarine threat. Even with restricted submarine attack, ships were being sunk faster than replacements could be built.

It is not the purpose here to describe how Germany nearly succeeded, but the blame for Britain being, for a period, within six weeks of starvation and surrender can firmly be placed at the Navy's door. The Admiralty's argument, categorically stated, was that there were just not enough escort warships to introduce convoys, despite that being a strategy which had served the country so well for centuries. Five thousand ships a week entered and left British ports. The primary duty of available escorts was cross channel reinforcements, the Grand Fleet (bent on a Trafalgar), the supply lines of welsh coal to French factories and to the fleet, and the

Jellicoe was appointed Commander in Chief of the Grand Fleet on the outbreak of war with Germany in 1914. He commanded the Fleet at the Battle of Jutland and though it was no Trafalgar the British Fleet, despite heavy losses, kept the sea and the German High Seas Fleet never really sortied again. Relieved in turn by Admiral Sir David Beatty, Jellicoe was First Sea Lord from December 1916 to January 1918 when he was dismissed by the First Sea Lord Sir Eric Geddes.

Jellicoe was described by Winston Churchill 'as the only man on both sides who could have lost the war in an afternoon', which is a fair summing up of his achievement at Jutland. After the war he was created Admiral of the Fleet Earl Jellicoe and did magnificent work touring the Empire. He was also largely responsible for advising the Government of Canada when that country came to establish a Navy (photograph courtesy IWM).

safeguarding of the iron ore from Norway. Lastly merchant skippers were adamant that apart from ships engaged on short voyages, station keeping in the Atlantic was impossible.

It took two years of war and the brains and courage of one rebellious commander, later a great Controller, Admiral Sir Reginald Henderson, despairingly working behind his superior's back, to make clear to the hierarchy that the number of ocean going vessels supplying Britain's war needs *from overseas* was usually less than 140 a week. This much lower figure was marginally within the number of small warships theoretically available to provide escorts for the ocean convoys in which the merchant ships could more safely voyage.

The Prime Minister, Mr Lloyd George, was always inclined to assert that it was his visit to the Admiralty in April 1917 that finally goaded a reluctant Board into adopting a general convoy system. It is true that a memorandum, prepared by Sir Maurice Hankey, the war cabinet secretary, on the basis of figures secretly supplied by Henderson, triggered the prime minister's unprecedented action. It is also true that Admiral Duff, recently charged by Jellicoe with the formation of an anti-submarine warfare division within the naval staff, had quickly reversed the objections he inherited. He had minuted Jellicoe, 'It seems to me evident that the time has arrived when we must be ready to introduce a comprehensive scheme of convoy at any moment'. On the following day, 27th April 1917,

Jellicoe approved it. On 30th April, Lloyd George visited the Admiralty. Nevertheless, full implementation of a convoy system still foundered on the belief that the primary duty of available escorts was the Grand Fleet; and that after a great Trafalgar, all would be well.

Hence, even with that decision of April 1917, the introduction of convoys took many weeks to materialise. By July the homeward bound convoys from the United States started to benefit; but months of dreadful sinkings ensued for outward bound ships for which no escorts could as yet be provided. Then Jellicoe, worn and increasingly pessimistic, helped to set in train a course of events leading to incomparable tragedy. At a war council meeting in June 1917 he suddenly announced, 'It is no good discussing plans for next Spring—we cannot go on'. In the following weeks he constantly returned to the theme that the Belgian coast must be cleared by the army, so that the German Flanders submarine flotillas would have to retreat to the High Seas fleet bases at Kiel and Wilhelmhaven. As these more northern bases were already accounting for 60% of sinkings, this measure would have helped, but perhaps not so much as hoped for. Nevertheless Jellicoe's advocacy moved the war council to adopt General Haig's plan for such an offensive; and the Navy undertook to land a division on the flank when the British army reached Roulers. The advance never materialised, because for seven dreadful weeks, it floundered, and finally foundered, in the mud and blood of Passchendaele.

None of this did the Navy any good in the eyes of those who knew the facts and, with the mounting casualties in Flanders on top of the already horrific losses, the cry, 'What is the Navy doing?' became manifest. It reached a peak when the Norwegian convoys were twice attacked, their escorts sunk and most of the precious merchantmen also. Then the *Goeben* and *Breslau*, having already, through British naval incompetence escaped from the Mediterranean to Turkey at the beginning of the war, suddenly came out of the Dardanelles and played havoc with British installations in the Aegean. The *Breslau* hit a mine and sank and *Goeben* ran aground, but even after six days of desultory bombing the latter managed to refloat herself and returned, in triumph, to Constantinople.

At last the war ended. There had been no Trafalgar. For the first time since 1667 there had been assaults from the sea on the soil of Britain. The already appalling Army casualty lists had mounted bloodily at Passchendaele in response to the Navy's admission that it could not save the country from starvation. Then the German skeleton crews in the surrendered High Seas fleet managed to scuttle their ships in Scapa Flow while the guardships were out on exercises. This act was of some benefit in solving the squabbles at the Peace Conference; but to the public it appeared as a fittingly inept end to a rather inglorious wartime performance by the Royal Navy. This public attitude was not lost on the Board of Admiralty and they sought a scapegoat.

Chapter 4
The Great Betrayal
1924–1925

I awoke from my armistice dream, and we all found ourselves in the rough, dark, sour and chilly waters in which we are swimming still.

Winston Churchill, some years after World War I

The years after World War I were sad ones for the United Kingdom. There were a few days of overwhelming excitement and then the reality of the blood spilt, and the treasure fired into the mud of Flanders hit the population like a poleaxe. All was not well. The Army had mutinied in London and burnt down the Town Hall in Luton. Those who had fought through the agony of trench or desert war had to be brought home, but Germany still had to be occupied. The Navy mutinied in the Baltic, where war was still being carried on against the Bolsheviks. The old industries were having difficulty getting going. Civilian wages were high; service pay, low. The Versailles peace treaty was being fought out in Paris largely on the basis that, whatever else, an already wholly bankrupt Germany must be further beggared, 'till the pips squeaked'. Cut-backs were the order of the day; war stocks of guns, aircraft and ships were being sold off for a song. The war profiteers were doing well. Those who had offered their lives and survived, many of them now maimed, expected a land fit for heroes. They looked in vain. Revolution was round the corner.

The Royal Navy's case was little better. England had been bombarded from the sea and nearly starved. The Royal Naval Air Service, the pioneers, with the Royal Engineers, of war in the air, had been snatched away. The newly created Royal Air Force was absorbing scarce resources and some emotional acclaim, both badly needed by the other services. The Treasury was in control, so perhaps the inertia exhibited by the Admiralty over the question of naval pay for a predominantly long engagement Navy (12 years, then 10 years) had some excuse. The solution finally agreed with the Treasury was to establish two different lower deck pay scales, one for those who were serving in 1919 and a different one for those who

31

joined later. This anomaly was to come home to roost at Invergordon in 1931. If there was some excuse for initial mistakes and lack of drive by tired men in the immediate aftermath of the war, there can be little or none for what happened in three areas of naval administration during the next decade.

The means whereby a fighting service is officered is fundamental to its effectiveness as an instrument of national policy, although the essential qualities which go to make up a satisfactory officer candidate are difficult to define or accurately to discern. The 'extended interview boards' founded in the 1940s (war office selection boards, or WOSBEES) were a move in the right direction and, as Fisher held, there is now no doubt that the necessary officer like qualities can be found in all sections of the population.

The first mistake of the post war Boards of Admiralty was their failure to build on the Fisher/Battenberg reforms for promotion from the lower deck. As Captain Roskill has written,

'If the attitude of the Admiralty towards the broadening of the democratic basis of bodies such as the 'welfare committee' was cautious, their approach to the question of widening the sources from which the officer entry was drawn was a good deal more so. During the war the question of opening the road to cadetships to able young men serving on the Lower Deck was raised, but nothing was done to expand the 'Mate' scheme which had been introduced as long ago as 1912.'

The director of naval training, Rear-Admiral Herbert Richmond, was not content with the stuffy outlook of his seniors and remained determined that suitable boy bluejackets (in the jargon of those days) should be withdrawn from the fleet and trained and educated to turn them into officers. The Second Sea Lord, responsible for personnel, was equally determined that 'to be a good officer it was necessary first to be a gentleman'. The context in which that view was minuted added fuel to the efforts of those anxious to circumvent recalcitrant Sea Lords. The argument found its way onto the agenda of an Admiralty Board meeting at which, of course, politicians were present. The other naval members seem to have been at least as cool to Richmond's bluejacket proposal as the Second Sea Lord, but this did not impress the political representatives. The matter was deferred and Mr McNamara, the Financial Secretary to the Admiralty, perhaps in the belief that the Christmas spirit might have softened their Lordship's hearts, circulated a memorandum on 20th December 1920 as follows,

> '*I suppose it will be admitted that the process of evolution develops a legitimate aspiration to commissioned rank on the part of humble folk. The statesmanlike policy is to meet the aspiration and lead it along lines that will be of the greatest advantage to the service. If that is not done the Board will wake up one fine morning to find that Parliament has determined upon immediate opportunities being given, which it may not then be possible, in the time at our disposal, to handle circumspectly.*'

In the best Admiralty tradition a committee was at once convened and quickly reported that 'indeed it was the case that the cost limited the selection of officers to a restricted and relatively wealthy class'.

No action followed, but there is always one last arrow in the quiver for those as determined as Richmond, and that is the contrived parliamentary question. Such a question was quickly arranged and the Board was stirred to another committee which reported even more quickly and more categorically that selection of boy bluejackets should be made as early as possible through the (special entry) public school scheme, which had been started in 1913.

The Board of Admiralty took this judgement on the chin, but the naval members returned to the fray with considerable subtlety. The Treasury was approached to obtain relief for those parents who could not afford to send their sons into the Navy either through the public school or Dartmouth entry. Put forward, as it was, in the context of the recommendations of the second committee, the Financial Secretary and the Treasury assumed that this would open the way for boy bluejackets but, as the fleet was not informed and no machinery established to select suitable candidates, none were forthcoming, and the Board once more emerged triumphant. The subsidy provided by the Treasury was, however, made available to parents of candidates such as this author's, who had lost whatever money they had in the war and were prepared to submit to a very probing and strict means test. Boy bluejackets had to wait another ten years till Mr A V Alexander and a Labour government carried forward the ideas that Admiral Prince Louis of Battenberg had put forward twenty years before.

'Having thus', as David Divine once so elegantly put it, 'in their view satisfactorily disposed of this evident assault on good order and naval discipline, Their Lordships turned their collective wisdom towards the problems of engineers and engineering'.

Manifestly, the Board of Admiralty felt that much of the criticism levelled at the Navy over the war years betokened a loss of 'the Nelson spirit'; a phrase said to be greatly in use at that time. Such loss the Board clearly attributed to the Selborne/Fisher reforms and, in particular, to a preoccupation with materiel matters to the exclusion of whatever else the Nelson spirit might have entailed. (This was regardless of the fact that Nelson, the beloved leader, also always watched the materiel state of his fleet most closely.) Further, the young new Fisher scheme trained officers were not yet sufficiently senior to have influenced, in any way whatever, naval policy, strategy or tactics during World War I. Nevertheless, egged on by some of the newly formed naval staff anxious to show their worth, the Board, having negated proposals to promote boy bluejackets, now set about dismantling Fisher's further ideas for an influential corps of naval engineers.

It is difficult seventy years later, to reproduce the controversy surrounding the new (E) and old-type engineers. Fisher was dead, but he had given engineers what they had hoped for and, best of all, a sense of mission by which they were inspired. Though the Fisher specialists, whether gunnery (G), torpedo (T), navigation (N) or engineering (E) were still young and very junior, the (E)s certainly assumed that equality of status was assured, even if some had doubts that complete interchangeability would ever be feasible. Promotion prospects and the chance for engineers to influence the war-fighting capability of the future navy were, they believed, set in concrete.

The first smoke signal that policies were changing further up the ladder came in the First Lord's speech to the House of Commons in 1920.

'There is definite distinction as regards knowledge and capabilities between those who are to be trained in the science of naval war and strategical and tactical methods of fighting and those who are to deal with the upkeep and maintenance of engineering and mechanical appliances which are necessitated by complex machinery and weapons of war. Each side requires a special study and for this reason final separation of the Branches is essential.'

Although the idea of 'sides' which Fisher abhorred was again injected into the debate there was logic in what the First Lord had to say. It was clear that Fisher's concept of the interpretive role that he believed should be provided by engineers, between thrusting science and technology in the civilian sector, and those non-technical seamen (executive) officers on the newly born naval staff who defined the needs and weapons of war at sea, had not yet penetrated the Admiralty Board room. Board members (and an unimaginative naval staff) still regarded engineers only as seagoing engine drivers. The First Lord's speech continued,

> *'The technique which he requires is in each case a means to an end. On the part of the executive officer this is the power to employ a weapon or direct movements or communications. The engineer officer, however, maintains the motive power but takes no part in the ultimate direction of the ship's movements. In this case maintenance is divorced from ultimate control; they are non-executive officers. The distinction therefore, in this respect between executive and non-executive officers is that the former, when they do control the means, control the end; the latter never do so.'*

Since Christmas 1914, when Fisher had returned to the Admiralty and had made the old type engineers 'military' by allowing them to wear the executive curl on their sleeves, five branches had existed within the officer structure; military (including the old type engineer and the new (E) officer), medical, accountant, naval instructor and artisan. By an Order in Council in 1925, which came to be called 'the great betrayal' in engineering circles in and outside the Navy, the five branches were abolished and twelve categories were established. These were executive officers, engineer officers, medical, dental and accountant officers, instructor officers, chaplains, shipwright, ordnance and electrical officers, schoolmasters and wardmasters. By employing the word categories the Admiralty hoped to avoid the stigma attached to those who were not executive (and therefore by tradition not military; and if not military then civilian). Gunners and gunners (T) and boatswains, although still warrant officers, were included in the executive category. Within this rather fraudulent device were several concealed caveats which gave the game away. Although for many years there had been an executive branch, this order, for the first time, gave legality to the term executive officer. Secondly the order made it clear that only executive officers were to be considered in the chain of command and stressed that all marks of respect, ceremonial guards, members of courts (later boards) of enquiry, courts-martial, and so on, and, importantly, command over ratings of all branches was to be reserved only for those in executive command. (In the mid 1950s the manning plans for ships and establishments still showed seamen chief and petty officers listed in the chain of command above all non-executive officers.)

If this constituted the smoke that blotted out the Fisher reforms, then the seat of the fire was in the newly constituted naval staff, as a few brief extracts from a contemporary Admiralty docket will reveal.

From the director of training and staff duties,

> 'The titles of Admiral, Commodore, Captain, Commander and Lieutenant have, from the days of Lord Nelson and before, until recent times, been clearly descriptive of officers who are qualified seamen. (*Author's note* Historically untrue. The Captain (Caput) was the top soldier on board, his Lieutenant (Locum Tenens) his second in command. The Master was the top seaman.) *The titles are as descriptive now as always, of officers on whom the safety of the ship depends, as well as the discipline, comfort and well being of all who sail in her. Titles which are not descriptive are meaningless. It is of the greatest importance that if the Navy is to uphold its tradition and maintain a rigid discipline ensuring a measure of content and general pride of service that the officers comprising the 'line of command', who are alone responsible, must first of all be seamen. Whilst those who are to succeed to high command must have exceptional gifts and leadership and, combined with these, judgement that can only come by long and varied experience of handling ships at sea...'*

After six further equally emotive paragraphs the director concluded,

> 'The desire of the engineer branch to obtain complete executive rank and uniform appears to be based on the mistaken assumption that a sailor's profession is not a profession at all and if this view is to be allowed to gain ground the Navy may fall more and more into the hands of the technical officer until the executive officer becomes the mere slave of the mechanical and material side. The fate of the Navy depends, and has always depended, on the professional development

of the highly skilled professional seamen personnel to keep the me-
chanical side, in regard to propulsion machinery and weapons, in
the proper objective direction to naval policy generally.'

The director of the gunnery division jumped in with that fearless
aplomb, sadly now lost, once regarded as emanating only from the
famous chummery generally known as 'Whaley', but more properly
Whale Island, the gunnery school or HMS *Excellent.* In flat
contradiction to the Fisher philosophy (and Fisher was one of the
godfathers of naval gunnery), he wrote,

> *'It is a waste of time for future engineers to spend time at Dartmouth.*
> *The naval atmosphere they are supposed to absorb merely makes*
> *them want to remain executive and dissatisfies them with the pros-*
> *pect of engineering. The mere fact of a different entry tends to keep*
> *the Branches separate from the start. Once the status of future engi-*
> *neers is laid down, ie separate entry Keyham, distinctive uniform*
> (*Author's note* Presumably as before, purple stripe, no execu-
> tive curl, special buttons) *titles as at present (engineer lieutenant*
> *etc; Author's note* Thus abolishing Fisher's (E) officer*) then an am-*
> *ple supply would be forthcoming. The type of people who feel that*
> *engineers suffer socially etc (sic) need not compete and we should be*
> *well rid of them.'*

The director of plans, Captain Dudley Pound took a more
objective view. Vice Admiral Sir Ronald Brockman, (then acting
Captain (S) R Brockman) whose father was one of the most famous
old type engineer officers, was secretary to Admiral Sir Dudley
Pound when the latter became First Sea Lord in 1939. Brockman
recalls that the docket on the status and responsibilities of engineer
and (E) officers was one of the first Pound sent for, to remind himself
of his views of fifteen years before. He had written,

> '...while it would be wrong to perpetuate a system on the score of ex-
> pediency which is wrong in principle and subservient (sic) of the
> general welfare of the Service, it would be even more wrong and
> even more damaging to the Service to embitter a large number of
> loyal and efficient officers by an act of seeming injustice. There can
> be no doubt that the present 'Old Scheme' engineer officers do set a
> high value on the titles to which, for many years they have aspired,
> and comparatively recently obtained.'

The director of naval intelligence veered towards Pound's way of thinking subject to the proviso that, 'besides having stripes of a particularly distinctive hue, engineers should also wear purple caps'!

So the future of naval engineers was tossed around and argued over, and the views of the naval staff were spread about the London clubs. On one side was the Engineer in Chief of the Navy, Engineer Vice Admiral Dixon, succeeded by Engineer Vice Admiral Skelton, and one member of the Board, Admiral, later Admiral of the Fleet Sir Henry Oliver. On the other were the rest of the naval members of the Board, the naval staff and senior civil servants. Between them the latter produced a Board memorandum which read,

The real question is a simple one. (*Author's note* A well known and now rarely used civil service ploy when dealing with a difficult problem for which only one solution is to be put forward.) *Is it or is it not for the good government of HM Navy* (the substitution of HM Navy for Royal Navy is another ploy, though never used today, implying that the Sovereign had been consulted or, if there was any dithering, would be consulted) *that officers of different branches who, by the nature of their employment are non-executive officers and can only have limited responsibility, should be invested with the same power, should be called by the same titles and be dressed in the same uniform and thus become indistinguishable from the executive officers of the ship who are responsible for the fighting efficiency, the general discipline and the faithful discharge of their duties by every branch of officer and rating in the ship...experience shows that it is of the utmost importance to discipline that officers of a ship who possess executive power should be easily distinguishable from those who have not...it is equally wrong for an officer who does not hold the qualification of a seaman to pass in the world as if he did. And it is obviously bad for discipline that officers who have never commanded so much as a cutter, let alone a ship or squadron, should be known as captain or admiral...'*

The memorandum concluded,

'On board and at official functions the engineer's position can be decreed. His position ashore or that of his wife cannot possibly be adjusted by regulations.'

The faults were not entirely one-sided. The tale is told of the engineer who disputed his First Lieutenant's right to go into dinner before him and received the rather chilling riposte, 'It doesn't matter at all to me whether you go into dinner before or after me. But all I can tell you ,Brown, is that my Ma will never ask your Ma to tea.'

Thanks in part to the fury of engineers and (E) officers and to Admiral Oliver's views, the Board did not carry out all these proposals fully. Nevertheless both types of engineer were relegated with the ten other categories to a lower plane and their influence thereby greatly reduced; while the importance of a naval engineer's interpretive function between science and galloping technology and sea warfare, if it was ever understood, which seems doubtful, was consigned to oblivion. Outside the Navy, the United Service Club (The Senior), whose stately buildings are now occupied by the Institute of Directors, and where Fisher's portrait still hangs, once again closed its doors to (E) officers as it had always done to old type engineers; and the expulsion of those (E) officers who had recently been allowed to join when they were still deemed military and on a par with executive officers was considered. A few (E)s resigned in protest when this became known, but the more wily, aware that the Senior was a good 'listening post' where they could probably hear what the seamen officers' caucus in the shape of The Navy Club of 1765 and 1785 (in Admiral Sir David Luce's words, 'the Navy's Monday Club') was up to, remained members anyway.

A personal reminiscence of a near mutiny may demonstrate to the non-naval reader the absurdities of the lack of so called 'military command' by non-executive officers. In a ship in the early 1950s, my senior engineering chief petty officer reported to me at about 1130 one forenoon that the Master at Arms, asserting (without proof) that a non-seaman petty officer had been responsible for vomiting in the petty officer's heads (lavatories) when drunk, had ordered a roster of sentries from amongst the non-seaman chief and petty officers to be posted, dressed in gaiters and belts, beside the door to the heads from noon onwards. My senior chief with the senior supply and medical dept chiefs (I was the most senior specialist commander), informed me that they were intending to refuse to obey this order which would bring them all and their petty officers into contempt with their subordinates. I agreed and asked the Master at Arms to rescind or postpone the order until I had been into the matter, which he refused to do pointing out, quite correctly, that I had no authority to order him to do so. Giving my senior chief a written order that he was not to comply, thereby myself taking full responsibility for his refusal to obey a legitimate order (as did my non-executive colleagues to their chiefs), I then had to interrupt the Captain and executive Commander during a session of Captain's defaulters and inform them that if the Master at Arms was not over-ruled by the executive Commander, he was proposing to charge the three senior chief petty officers concerned with mutiny. The order was at once revoked, but tempers were high and it was in the tropics. Altogether it was a close shave.

The relegation of engineers to their old inferior position had four easily discernible consequences.

1. The majority of those offering themselves as officer candidates through the special (public school) entry opted for the executive category as their first choice. The (E) entry had to depend largely on 'second choicers' who had failed to secure sufficient marks in the entrance examination. This narrowed the field of engineers with higher than average intellectual ability.

2. Propaganda at Dartmouth, by the older academics and the executive term officers was reinforced. It constantly emphasised the lowly place held by engineers in the Navy and stopped (until the mid 1930s) all but a very few enthusiasts or those who developed eye problems, from opting or being drafted into (E). *

3. The naval staff became an élite within an executive élite, two steps rather than one above the (E) officer, so there was no meeting of minds between those who were (alleged to be) studying war and those who should have been seeking the keys to potentially better mobility and weapons.

4. Many of the old type engineers withdrew into a sullen laager and failed to develop the links with science and industry outside their immediate purview, which should have been their main function. While the younger (E)s left the Navy for a great welcome in industry, or bided their time till they were more senior.

There remain two more sagas of gross neglect by post World War I Boards which were to have appalling consequences in World War II, one concerning electricity and the other fuel.

When electricity was introduced into the Navy in the late nineteenth century, some sailors were electrocuted. Ships were lit by electricity and searchlights, signal lamps and navigation lights used electricity, although oil lamps were kept ready as standby in case

---

*Although such propaganda diminished in the 1930s it was reawakened during the 1939 war by retired officers on the staff at Dartmouth and (after Dartmouth was bombed) at Eaton Hall. A very senior retired (E) officer recalled when reading this in draft how, when he volunteered for (E) in 1946 he was asked if he did not realise that by doing so he was condemning himself to three steps down in the social scale!

such a new fangled device failed. Guns were electrically fired (though additional mechanical means were always provided) and ventilation fans were driven by electricity, as were submersible pumps fitted in the bigger ships after Jutland. Submarines, when submerged were driven by batteries re-chargeable only when the submarine surfaced. However, for the elevating of big guns and the training of turrets and the operation of cranes and derricks the Navy emulated Tower Bridge, or lifts, in London and used hydraulic systems instead. In general, the application of electricity to naval warfare, and particularly weapons was entirely neglected. Like steam a few years before Their Lordships felt it a novelty best ignored.

The director of electrical engineering, a purely civilian department in the Admiralty, was responsible for the design of all electrical machinery and equipment and for the distribution systems and their installation. The feedback from sea experience was minimal. The old type engineer and (E) specialists were responsible to the Engineer in Chief for the design, installation and maintenance at sea of the steam or diesel engines which drove the dynamos. The executive officer with a (T) torpedo specialisation, advised by a warrant electrician or electrical artificer, was responsible for the distribution of all electrical power on board.

There were many (T) and (E) specialists who realised the great benefits which would accrue to the Navy's war fighting potential if electricity could be adopted on a much wider scale. But the question of ultimate responsibility was the rock on which agreement foundered. Between 1918 and 1925 four powerful committees examined the problem and as might be expected in the climate of the time, divided on executive/non-executive lines. To add to the problems the Navy was suffering savage cuts amongst executive officers and any extra responsibility for (T) specialists, it was anticipated, might help them to weather the storm. There was intense lobbying and furious argument. Three main schemes emerged from the first three committees.

Scheme One

The Torpedo (T) specialisation should carry all responsibility for electrical generation and distribution, the dividing line between (T) and (E) being the coupling (including the coupling bolts which would belong to the (E)s) between the dynamo and its engine, whether steam or diesel.

This scheme's difficulty was that it would mean a more lengthy training for (T) officers which might militate against their capability as seamen and therefore against their chances of promotion, so scheme two was proposed.

Scheme Two

This was basically scheme one, except that, to avoid the extra training for (T) officers, additional civilian electrical engineers would be entered into the the Admiralty, thus providing a reservoir of 'electrical engineering advisers', who would be given temporary naval rank at sea to advise the ship's (T) officer, who would have ultimate responsibility.

Scheme Three

(Strongly advocated by the Engineer in Chief and, after half a century of argument, the practice now prevailing). This recommended that the newly forming (E) structure should be numerically reinforced to take over all the fleet's high power electrical responsibilities. The necessary training in electrical engineering being added on to the mechanical engineering training then being given at the recently re-opened RN Engineering College at Keyham, Devonport. Subsequently, for a few, an advanced design course, analagous to the mechanical engineering 'dagger' course, would be instituted at the RN College at Greenwich, where the civilian electrical engineers were also trained.

With the Geddes axe hanging over executive officers and the 'great betrayal' threatening (E) officers, both sides fought their corners with relentless venom. Finally the Board of Admiralty set up its very own (Board) working party to try to cut this Gordian knot—and dreamed up a fourth scheme based on the following premises.

1. It would be a retrograde step for any executive (T) specialist to be responsible for any form of engineering. (To give them their due this was not the view of many (T) specialists. It was HMS *Vernon* (the torpedo school) which strongly influenced the establishment of a Signals School. (T) specialists were amongst the least biased against the use of up to date technology in the fleet.)

2. It was unthinkable that the mechanical cuckoos in the nest, the Fisher (E) officers, who the Board were only just managing to tame, should arrogate to themselves more actual power in the fighting arrangements of warships, by assuming greater responsibilities and by adding to their numbers.

3. With 1 and 2 in mind and on the principle of divide and rule, the Board decided that there should be a new type of engineer the (EE) (electrical engineering) officer. Furthermore, to make sure that there should be no more Fisher nonsense about interchangeability or equality of status with executive officers, (EE) officers would devote their whole careers to the development of electricity in the Royal Navy. However, to pacify the various contestants a remarkable training programme was envisaged.

> a. The (EE) officer would do two years identical training with (E) officers at the RN Engineering College at Keyham, followed by one further year there studying electricity.
>
> b. From Keyham the (EE) officer would go to Greenwich for a further two years training in electrical engineering with the civilian electrical engineers training for Admiralty design work.
>
> c. The training of (EE) officers in their sixth year, would culminate with one year of training with (T) executive officers in HMS *Vernon*, the torpedo school.

However the Board lost its nerve and this remarkable apparition, though it appears in a draft Admiralty Fleet Order, never saw the light of day. All this activity made it clear to the Engineer in Chief that the electrical syllabus at the RN Engineering College must be broadened. As the amount of electrical machinery within the engineering department and therefore unarguably the responsibility of (E) officers at sea increased, the late 1920s saw the start of training for engine room artificers (electrical) and stokers (electrical) who would be responsible to their own (E) officers for maintaining all the electrical machinery essential for mobility, habitability and the control of damage.

The other near fatal omission in Fisher's engineering reforms was concerned with the changing of the whole fleet from coal to oil fuel. Although this change was gradually implemented, the three cardinal principles laid down by the Royal Commission on Fuel and Engines were forgotten, as will be recounted in chapters 9 and 10.

This chapter has described how the post World War I Boards of Admiralty abrogated many of Fisher's reforms or failed to follow his recommendations. These actions taken in all sincerity as being good for the Navy, were founded on the mistaken belief that Fisher's legacy of some community of knowledge and a lifelong community of sentiment between engineers and seamen officers, had somehow been responsible for a large part of the naval failure in World War I.

Fisher's philosophy, stressing the need to widen the field of officer recruitment and for all officers to have a greater understanding of technical matters, together with his belief that the status and influence of engineers needed to be enhanced, was the rub. These ideas, the Sea Lords believed, were combining to poison the sacred chalice of naval tradition from which great seamen and superb leaders alone could be drawn.

As a result, advancing naval technology withered. Its application to surface and air warfare was neglected and against the submarine threat too optimistically regarded; the need for better mobility, the glory of the great age of sail, forgotten. Thus in 1939 when war came with, yet again, a newly built German navy and unrestricted air and submarine warfare, the Royal and Merchant Navies suffered unprecedented human casualties as well as losses of ships and cargo which almost brought defeat to Britain. This disaster can be directly attributed in large part to these unhappy Board decisions, to the transfer of the Royal Naval Air Service to the RAF, and to a restrictive web of international treaties, too lightly entered into by short-sighted politicians who failed, as they still fail, to understand that Britain is a maritime nation. And so, once more in 1942, but this time through no fault of the Navy, the Battle of the Atlantic was almost lost, Britain was nearly starved of food and the sinews of war; and for the second time this century Germany saw a European, and perhaps a world, hegemony within the Fatherland's grasp.

In writing of the political scene between 1931 and 1935, Winston Churchill referred to that period as 'the locust years'. Such a description can equally well be applied to the naval affair between 1919 and 1932, particularly as regards the deliberate neglect of the application of new technology to modern maritime war. After that, Admirals Chatfield, Kelly, WW Fisher, James, Dudley Pound, Fraser, Cunningham and others, once more stirred the moth eaten organism into which, as in the pre-Fisher era, the Royal Navy had retreated, and made it at least spiritually, ready to do battle. Not even Admiral Sir Reginald Henderson, one of the three great Third Sea Lords and Controllers of the Navy this century, could restore, by 1939, the technological momentum that the locust years had dissipated; although he gave his life through overwork in a desperately brave attempt to do so.

Chapter 5
The Locust Years
1919–1932

Looked at from the purely strategical point of view the standard of British Naval strength might be sought in those principles which had determined such strength during the preceding centuries. Those principles may be crytallised in a few words: words which, in one or another form, recur constantly in the contemporary discussions: the fighting forces of the British Navy should be of sufficient strength to ensure the safety...of its sea communications, in all reasonably probable world conditions.

The agreement made at the Washington Conference in 1921/22 constituted a complete departure from the traditional principles of British security at sea.

Statesmen and Sea Power
Admiral Sir Herbert Richmond

The negating of the hopes of the new (E) officers, the refusal to countenance more promotion from the lower deck and the aborting of an electrical engineering branch almost at the moment of birth, were only some of the self induced policy manifestations of a deepening malaise in the post World War I Navy. The Sea Lords seemed to believe that the ideas that Fisher had promoted were inimical to seamanlike tradition from which alone the Navy's leaders should be drawn, so no longer should such reforms be permitted to continue. As a result, in the immediate aftermath, as discussed here and in chapter 6, naval technology withered. From the politicians came another series of blows. Against the views of the Admiralty and the Army Board, the Smuts committee had recommended, and the government had agreed, that the Royal Naval Air Service with the Army's Royal Flying Corps, between them the pioneers of air warfare, should be snatched from their parent services. The newly created Royal Air Force then absorbed scarce resources and, amongst politicians, the principal accoucheurs, great support.

The Washington Naval Treaty sent twenty great capital ships to the breaker's yard, caused the four super-Hoods to be dismantled on the stocks and thus, twenty years later, contributed to disaster in the Far East. Subsequent politically inspired treaties governing cruiser and flotilla strengths cast aside the whole teaching of history as well as the painful lessons of experience. Instead the numbers and classes of ships were related to the (irrelevant) strength of the United States and French navies rather than to the task of keeping Britain from starvation, which is always the main burden the Navy will have to carry in any war.

With the post-war boom conditions, until the recession of 1930, the position of the well trained seaman or artificer who left the Navy was rosy, but the 1930 slump, with soaring unemployment figures, put an end to that. Their prospects in civil life became grim.

Among naval officers and ratings a feeling of desperation began to develop. At the armistice there were about 190,000 regular officers and ratings in the Service. By 1931 this had been reduced to less than 90,000, nearly 60,000 fewer than before the war. There was also the Geddes axe. More than 1200 lieutenants and lieutenant command-ers, ill-advisedly entered by the Admiralty as regulars in the early and immediate pre-war years, were cast from their chosen career and thrust into a world they did not know, with a farcical gratuity and a negligible pension that they were disastrously encouraged to commute. The pathetic and penniless future of so many fine war experienced naval officers who had been thrown onto the scrap heap, aroused a feeling of doom and uncertainty among those who were left.

For those sailors and stokers who stayed in the Navy the future was also not very promising. After an intolerable delay, pay was raised by only 120% from pre-war days against an inflation rate of 250%. This gave an able seaman 28/- a week against nearly 55/- for a builder's labourer. That was not all. In the pre-war days a commission abroad, certainly for a married man, was always followed by a commission at home or, better still, a commission in barracks or a training establishment in a home port, probably near the rating's home, to which he could return for three nights out of four. Postwar problems caused the drafting arrangements to fall into disarray. Men just back from a foreign commission would find themselves, after their leave, en route once more to some other far

flung corner of the world; and the period spent in barracks was
frequently only a matter of hours.

With officers already deeply unhappy and unusually pre-occu-
pied with their own problems, leadership faltered, and nowhere
more so than in the Atlantic Fleet where one third of each ship's crew
had to be changed every four months, such was the drafting chaos.
There was no time for divisional officers to get to know those
committed to their charge.

Naval discipline, hitherto reasonably well maintained, began to
wobble. Initially it faltered in the Baltic where HMS *Cicala*, a river
gunboat, very reluctantly sailed against the Bolsheviks only after the
senior officer present threatened to blow her out of the water with
the guns from a monitor. Bolshevik propaganda was rife in the UK
and sailors from one ship due to sail for the Baltic deserted in
Devonport, but reached only as far as Paddington before being
arrested. HMS *Vindictive* was nearly wrecked when stokers tried to
shut off steam to the fans supplying air to the boiler furnaces just as
the anchor had been weighed; but a young engineer officer armed
with a heavy wheel spanner drove them out of the fan flat just in
time. The Baltic was not the only mutiny. Hostilities only (HO)
ratings demanded to be released as soon as the armistice was signed
and their disaffection spread to regular ratings. There were many
anomalies in gratuities for war service, with a considerable
difference between those ratings who had served at sea or ashore,
although in the case of officers as was only too plain to the sailors,
there was no such distinction. And so matters rumbled on in a
thoroughly unsatisfactory way. Then there was a very real mutiny in
HMS *Lucia*. This, in early January 1931 came shortly after Ramsay
MacDonald, the then Prime Minister, was reported as having
overruled the Board of Admiralty over the signing of the London
Naval Treaty, whose conditions were a further step towards the
abandonment of the country's defences. This treaty not only
abrogated the agreement previously reached between the Government and the Admiralty but bad drafting made it impossible even to
maintain the numbers of ships stipulated, and France and Italy
anyway refused to be bound by major portions of it.

Though there was no direct connection between the treaty and
the mutiny on board HMS *Lucia*, the latter being a classic case of
unimaginative officers and less than tactful local orders, the
combination of the two events created the view that the Board of

Admiralty were less than effective, if not patently incompetent. When, as a result of the treaty, it became clear that another four battleships were to be broken up and further cuts in personnel were to be made, morale slumped to rock bottom.

The mutiny at Invergordon later in the year was another prime example of politicians overruling the Board (several of whom, it being August, regrettably were absent from their place of duty and on the moors), and it was bad luck that the C in C himself developed appendicitis as his flagship was about to put to sea. Stupidity on the part of his staff effectively ensured that his second in command was not supplied with the information concerning the immediate pay cuts ordered by the Government; cuts that were absurdly and fatally weighted against the more lowly paid sailors and, in the end, made known to them only by the radio and newspapers, while their officers remained in total ignorance of any official statement. The radio and press reports appeared to show that the lowest paid sailors were to have their pay cut by 25% and the officers by, at the most 10%. While this was not the whole truth it was near enough to be desperately disturbing, especially for married men. As a result, much of the Atlantic fleet refused orders to sail for exercises from Invergordon.

The mutiny was not a unique event, but rather the culmination of a steadily mounting number of traumatic incidents of ill-discipline and gross mismanagement by the Treasury, politicians and, not least, the Board of Admiralty itself. The post war Boards were not far wrong when they diagnosed a lack of the Nelson spirit, but they misunderstood Nelson. It was creative imagination that naval leadership lacked in the 1920s. A hesitancy or total inability at the top to come to terms with evolving twentieth century society appears to have been the main fault, and not, as so many senior officers believed, the Fisher legacies. By betraying his legacies the Boards added to their own difficulties and damaged the future fighting efficiency of the Navy.

Outwardly the mutiny at Invergordon did the Navy and the country great harm, but there was enough time before war came, and enough great officers, to heal the rift between the lower deck's justifiable revulsion at the conduct of naval administration and to give the service the leadership it deserved and craved. In the end, however, the time was too short to make up the backlog of technology that had failed to be applied to fighting efficiency, to correcting the practices that had grown up preventing real advance and to try to undo the shackles of politically motivated treaties which made naval nonsense.

Ship design, hampered by treaties, was in the hands of a number of tribes whose 'frontiersmen' were apt to man the barricades against professional trespass. At the top of the tree was the newly born naval staff, an executive haven despised by the seagoing officer. While the staff and the engineers quarrelled, the Director of Naval Construction quietly installed himself as the principal technical adviser to the Board, although in Sir John Fisher's day it is clear this eminence had been shared with the Engineer in Chief of the Navy.

It is sometimes said that some of the failures in British ship design since the Tennyson D'Eyncourt (World War I) era of brilliant naval architecture have been due to the system of entry for naval constructors in the aftermath. This entry was largely limited to the very cleverest and hardest working of the dockyard shipwright apprentices. While there was no lack of intellectual ability their rather restricted background and upbringing, it is alleged, gave the majority of them an insufficiently broad outlook. The RN Engineering College at Keyham did not help interdependence between the two professions either. Young constructors studied in the dockyard and were permitted to eat their meals with the (E)s in the Keyham mess, but just as from sheer snobbery the United Service Club had banned (E)s from its doors, so, for much the same reason, the (E)s banned constructors from Keyham mess life in the ante-rooms, at least till Commander (E) C P Berthon returned as Dean (and Mess President) in 1934 and brought them fully into the life of the College. It took another thirty years before a Naval Constructor was admitted to the Imperial Defence College and even then he was not permitted to wear uniform when other students were required to do so. Successive Directors of Naval Construction came to regard themselves as the technological Popes to whom, they seemed to assume, the Engineer in Chief (uniformed) and the Director of Electrical Engineering (civilian) should always defer; while the able Royal Naval Scientific Service (RNSS) were considered of use in their development of the anti-submarine device known as ASDIC, but were otherwise and quite wrongly regarded by most engineers and constructors, as living on another planet.

If the above were not enough to hinder imaginative thought there were other major problems in the slowly emerging naval technological world. Among the problems were the following.

1. The ten year gap in the training cycle of naval engineers due to the closing of Keyham for engineering training in 1910 and its reopening for the new (E) specialists a whole decade later.

2. The fight over the status and career prospects of the (E) specialists which diverted so much time and attention from machinery design and development, thus diminishing the respect for naval engineering in industry, which Fisher had begun to build up.

3. The grip of the shipbuilders and machinery manufacturers on the department of the Engineer in Chief. Like the naval construction department, this was largely staffed by faithful but often 'blinkered' officers and civilians whose morale had sunk as a result of Board decisions.

4. Inadequate input of practical sea experience to the civilian department of electrical engineers.

5. The lack of any clear division of responsibility for weapon development and, importantly, gunfire control, between the gunnery division of the naval staff, HMS *Excellent* (the naval gunnery school), the Director of Naval Ordnance, the RNSS, engineering officers specialising in ordnance and torpedoes, Vickers (the prime contractors for most weapons) and Barr and Stroud (rangefinders and periscopes).

6. The web of international treaties constraining the size and firepower of warships, to which Britain, unlike Germany and other nations, religiously adhered.

7. Lack of money for the Royal Navy; and Treasury interference.

Mobility had been one of the great glories of the Navy in Nelson's day, when wind was the motive power. 'I went on shore', Nelson wrote, 'for the first time since June 1803; and for having my foot out of *Victory* two years, wanting ten days'. But wind gave way to coal, a world wide complex of coaling stations, a fleet of colliers to supply them and terrible labour by ships' companies to embark it. Churchill, on Fisher's recommendation, started to change the fleet from coal to oil. But in the 1920s and 1930s the warnings about oil burning equipment that Fisher gave were disregarded and the the potentially great advance in mobility, if oil fuel could be embarked from tankers while under way, was never pursued.

The result of the hilarious tug of war in 1845 between HMS *Alecto*, paddle driven, and HMS *Rattler*, a propeller driven sloop of approximately the same horsepower and tonnage, is well known. The *Rattler* won. With true Admiralty scepticism this did not entirely convince their Lordships. After four years of deep consideration of such a grave matter they tied HMS *Basilisk* and HMS *Niger* together. Again the propeller won, so propellers had come to stay and paddles were out. We are concerned here with the state of the fleet when it went to war in 1939 and why it was so technologically backward. Unhappily, between 1919 and 1932 the same sceptical outlook on evolving technology as that of the previous century still obtained; and those engineers who might have seen what should be done had so little influence that there was hardly any movement at all.

The basic training of the old type engineers ceased when Keyham was closed in 1910, but it was still possible for a select few, until the supply ran out, to undergo the later advanced training at Greenwich resulting in a 'dagger' against their name in the Navy List. There was a gap until the (E) stream started once more in the 1920s.

Before, during and after World War I, a system had evolved whereby certain of these (old type) 'dagger' engineers became earmarked for careers centred on their professional engineering performance in the department of the Engineer in Chief, rather than on their overall performance as naval officers and engineers at sea and ashore. The former came to regard themselves as an élite corps, strongly hierarchical because the older they were the more experienced they became in the conduct of headquarters business and thus were assumed to be technically superior to their juniors; and certainly superior to their contemporaries at sea who, in practice, were banned from this magic circle. In plain terms, Moses, in the shape of the Engineer in Chief, handed down the tablets to his immediate and personally selected acolytes, whose future depended on ensuring his instructions were meticulously obeyed. Later, when (E) officers started to achieve some seniority, this anomalous situation was recognised and career records and importantly, career planning were removed from the Engineer in Chief and placed, like those of executive officers, under the Second Sea Lord. The latter was given an 'extra naval assistant for engineering personnel' (EAP), comparable to his naval assistant who, in collaboration with the specialist schools, carried out similar duties for the executive specialisations. Although this augured well for the future, it was not till the the late 1930s, with a few notable exceptions, that any perceptible change in the broadening of the professional outlook of the engineering hierarchy started to re-emerge.

Machinery reliability had always been the paramount policy, in some ways not a bad one, but it came to imply a marked reluctance to move forward at all and take advantage of any new technology; and the use of new technology was something on which Fisher had always insisted. To achieve serviceability a massive supply of spare gear was carried on board each ship, supplemented by a world wide complex of bases with dockyards and spare gear stores. With this back-up, Fisher's superlatively trained artificers and mechanicians, and restrictions on fuel expenditure due to the national economic climate, and therefore minimal seatime, the Engineer in Chief could point with some pride to the high degree of machinery reliability his department consistently provided. As class followed class of destroyers, cruisers, battleships and carriers, all built to complicated treaty provisions, only minor improvements were incorporated, the machinery manufacturer or shipbuilder having to be persuaded in every case to accept full responsibility for each hesitant move forward. In this process the Engineer in Chief's 'dagger' hierarchy grew closer and closer to their conservative opposite numbers in the shipbuilding industry and together they combined to form a cosy, cooperative, unadventurous and rather self satisfied coterie. Each 'Inspector', (a title dating from the days of 'inspectors of machinery afloat') in charge of a section in the Engineer in Chief's department supervising the machinery for a class of warship, was closely tied to his opposite number in the shipbuilding/marine engineering firm concerned, whose organisation and drawing office his HQ 'section' precisely paralleled.

The Engineer in Chief also supervised an outstation known as 'The Admiralty Fuel Experimental Station' (AFES) at Haslar, near Gosport. This establishment successfully optimised the burning of premium grade Persian fuel and improved the efficiency of highly forced naval boilers by the redesign of aids to water/steam circulation. But chemical treatment of boiler water to inhibit boiler corrosion was decried and Fisher's warnings of the dangers of concentrating on one particular fuel wholly ignored. Until a 'boiler specialist section' was established at headquarters, the AFES received little or no direction and became very much a 'one man band', going its own (in theory) very interesting way. Unfortunately much of that way, as it turned out, was later found to be of little or no practical use to a wartime fleet existing on fuels for which the AFES designed burning equipment was unsuited.

Apart from the organisational maze described above there were two major factors militating against better mobility of the British fleet. Before World War I, when steam turbine machinery was starting to supersede reciprocating machinery, Sir Charles Parsons ensured by his licence agreements that most shipbuilders manufactured steam turbines *only* to his basic design. This, on top of the Engineer in Chief's arrangements and the 'machinery reliability policy', implied a virtual standstill in turbine design which the Navy too placidly accepted. However Parsons had also set up a firm of land (power station) turbine designers, and after he died that firm developed independently. Thus from the same roots, but due to competition for cheap electric power, there evolved a flourishing UK power station industry which, in terms of efficiency, was well ahead of a marine turbine industry still in the strictly licensed hands of the shipbuilders.

Much the same was happening with boilers although here the power station industry had a great advantage in not being space restricted. Power station boilers could be larger than naval boilers, whose 'forcing rate' had to be much higher for the same steam output. (A simplistic analogy would be a painter's blowlamp for a naval furnace and a more gentle flame for that of the power station.) However power station boilers were years ahead in terms of boiler water treatment. By the injection of certain chemicals power station boilers could be steamed for 12–18 months before the massive task of internal cleaning to prevent tube and boiler drum corrosion became essential. With the smaller naval boilers in which the safety margins were less and corrosion, due to the high forcing rate could be expected earlier, the Engineer in Chief, advised by the AFES at Haslar, stuck resolutely to a formula related to the earlier days of steam propulsion when much less pure boiler water was the norm than had become general in recent years. This formula firmly excluded the use of chemicals and required that after 21 day's steaming (a day's steaming being defined as any day on which, for however long or short a period, boiler feed water had been admitted to the boiler) the boiler should be opened up and cleaned. Boiler cleaning was not as simple an operation as it sounds. It involved removing, through a very small manhole, all internal gear (of which in highly forced naval boilers there was a great deal), the blackleading and polishing of the internal surfaces of the boiler drums, the identifying of any corrosion pits which had to be precisely measured and charted on a plan, and then each of the thousands of tubes had to be cleaned individually by a revolving brush on a long cable (which was apt to break, involving much time to extract the brush). Subsequently each tube had to be scrupulously checked personally by the chief artificer boilermaker, who dropped a ball bearing down each to his mate in the lower boiler drum, to ensure there was no obstruction. (A blocked tube would inevitably mean lack of circulation, a burst tube and probable casualties). Simultaneously the soot had to be removed from outside the tubes, brick furnaces rebuilt and all valves refitted.

By the start of World War II the mobility of the fleet was poor for four reasons. The shipbuilders' turbine monopoly, too easily accepted by the Engineer in Chief, greatly reduced (in motoring parlance) the fleet's 'miles per gallon'. A refusal by the Engineer in Chief to countenance a chemical boiler water treatment, long proven in the power station industry, severely restricted the periods when ships were at immediate operational readiness, and was also the cause, of unnecessarily frequent and intensely hard and unpleasant work under trying conditions for boiler room crews, always living in a fog of asbestos dust from steam pipe and boiler insulation. The fleet was equipped to burn only premium grade fuel from the Persian Gulf. Finally, the fleet had neither practiced embarking, nor been fitted to embark, fuel at sea, from tankers, while underway.

Diesel propulsion as an alternative to steam had always interested Fisher; and Vickers too. With the Engineer in Chief's department divided into ship type sections, diesels had become immured in the submarine section and at an outstation called the Admiralty Engineering Laboratory (AEL), West Drayton. The state of the art in the UK had never progressed as far or as fast as on the Continent or in America. The British Merchant Navy relied largely on steam, derived from Welsh coal, driving reciprocating engines and, where diesels were fitted, they were so large as to be unsuitable for warships. Other than HMS *Adventure* a diesel propelled minelayer, no large diesel warships were built and the Admiralty restricted diesels to submarines and ships' boats; while in practice, the emergency diesel generators in battleships and battlecruisers were only rarely used. Although naval engineers visited Burmeister and Wain in Copenhagen and MAN and Sulzers, such contacts were always in connection with improvements in submarine propulsion.

Another reason for the neglect of diesels was that the necessary maintenance skills in the fleet were lacking. All officers and artificers on going to sea had first to qualify for their watchkeeping certificates in steam ships. Thereafter, if they volunteered for submarines and became diesel experienced, then in submarines they mostly stayed. Diesels in fact, apart from submarines, were rather a lost cause in the pre-World War II Navy. So much so that most classes of cruisers and destroyers even lacked emergency diesel generators. In war the failure of steam dynamos due to battle damage to a steam line, and in the absence of a self contained power unit such as a diesel generator, could mean, and, as was to be painfully discovered, sometimes did mean, the unnecessary loss of the ship.

It seems that the mutiny at Invergordon was the nadir of the post World War I Navy. Once that was past the Navy was fortunate in its new leadership under Admiral, later AF, Lord Chatfield (*chapter 6*) who, with several other new brooms righted so many wrongs in the re-establishment of discipline and improved personnel administration. In the wider field of naval affairs there remained a malaise. Other than armoured deck carriers, which were to prove their worth, and a remarkable submarine with a 15" gun, and another with an aircraft (neither of which, after trials, were repeated, although the Japanese made great use of submarine carried seaplanes in the wide wastes of the Pacific ocean), there was a lack of engineering or ship design innovation. The departments responsible, largely composed of people whose status and influence had risen under Fisher but had now once more dramatically been reduced, tended to cut themselves off in a self satisfied professional fortress. They were certainly parochially minded, apt to war with each other, badly hamstrung in design by politically imposed treaties, starved of money and lacking in intelligent direction from a newly formed, unimaginative and technically illiterate naval staff. Not surprisingly in the materiel field, between them all, there was a failure to provide the Navy with the mobility, battle damage resistance, weapons or control systems it so desperately needed. The 1920s were indeed the years that the locusts had eaten.

Part 2   The Long Climb Back

Chapter 6
Seeds of a Naval Engineering Revolution 1930–1940

No great improvements in the lot of mankind are possible, until a great change takes place in the fundamental constitution of their modes of thought.

Autobiography
John Stuart Mill

The Germans believed (and Guderian, the father of the Panzer troops, had ceaselessly taught) that they should regard the engine of a tank as a weapon, like a gun.

And We Shall Shock Them
General Sir David Fraser

The phrase 'winds of change' has become a cliché. Nevertheless it was winds of change, blowing from several directions, which merged into a climate of change amongst those who would come to deal with the Navy's technology especially that element affecting mobility.

Perhaps Invergordon was the first wind of change. To a great extent it did for the Navy what Dunkirk did nine years later for the Army. The whole service had to have a change in its attitude and its top direction. Admiral Sir Ernle Chatfield, Beatty's Flag Captain at Jutland, was brought back from his post as Commander in Chief Mediterranean Fleet, where the discipline was good, to become First Sea Lord. Admiral Sir John Kelly, brought back from retirement it has always been held on the direct orders of the Sovereign, took over the troublesome Atlantic (soon to be) Home Fleet. Rear-Admiral

(Bubbles*) James relieved the unfortunate Tomkinson who, as second in command in the absence of his superior, had been in charge. In the Mediterranean, 'the tall Agrippa', Admiral Sir William Fisher, probably the greatest leader of them all, took over from Chatfield, with Rear-Admiral A B Cunningham commanding his destroyers. If they were not all of them Fisher trained, they were of his era and battle wise.

In December 1934 Italy invaded Abyssinia, and soon a reinforced Mediterranean Fleet was on a semi-war footing based on Alexandria, as Malta was too close to Italy. Trouble was later to spread to the Western Mediterranean when the Spanish civil war broke out on 18th July 1936. Italian submarines started indiscriminate sinking of merchant ships as Italian and German airpower aided the Franco forces, while Soviet Russia backed the government. Much of the newly constituted Home Fleet found itself based on Gibraltar rather than on its home ports. In the Far East, Japan was attacking China, had resigned from the League of Nations, was advancing up the Yangtse, had denounced the Washington Treaty, had laid down the biggest and most heavily gunned battleship ever built (18.1" guns), had shelled HMS *Ladybird*, a Yangtse gunboat, and, finally, had started harassing Western shipping. It was clear that peace in that area was increasingly fragile. The Royal Navy's new leaders all foresaw that war was inevitable in Europe although less attention was paid to the Far East because Singapore was regarded as the unconquerable bastion. Recalling the failures of Jutland, WW Fisher and Cunningham, in particular, taught the Navy to fight at night as no other navy in the world could do in those pre-radar days.

The counter weapons and tactics for an adequate anti-air capability could not be developed, because the Navy had been deprived of its organic airpower. The cost in lives and ships of this failure, for once not the fault of the Admiralty, was to be great.

Another significant wind of change in the early to mid 1930s was the reversal of the dominant 'anti-(E)' attitude amongst Dartmouth cadets. Three reasons seem probable. Britain had been in a major depression. The Geddes axe was still in the minds of parents and cadets, and if there was another axe then an engineering qualification would be a valuable asset in civilian life. (Dartmouth apart this was also apparent to schoolmasters, and the proportion of 'first choice' (E) entrants through the 'special (non-Dartmouth) public school en-

*As a child he had been the model for the Pears Soap advertisement.

try', hitherto minimal, increased in the 1930s.) Added to this there was the subliminal influence at Dartmouth of the high quality (E) officers appointed to the staff: Commander (E) C H Nicholson; Lieutenant Commanders (E) Rebbeck, Roper and Marshall amongst others. All of them were either 'Fisher' trained or imbued with his philosophy. They were allowed no part in the sadistic disciplinary routines, which was in their favour; but in addition they always appeared to the cadets to be relaxed and humorous individualists. Lastly some of the very elderly academics, steeped in the *Britannia* traditions, anti-Fisher almost to a man, finally reached the end of the road. Their successors had no such memories and were of the postwar generation. One of these at least, the late Mr Mark Sugden, an international rugger player of great renown, knew many rugger playing (E) officers and was always a strong influence towards greater mutual understanding between Dartmouth and Keyham, between executive and engineer.

It was an even stronger 'wind' that helped to trigger a change towards a more 'pro-(E)' attitude amongst cadets at Dartmouth. The post Invergordon belief that naval leadership had crumbled brought a press and parliamentary demand for sail training. The clear out of the Board of Admiralty had brought Admiral Chatfield as First Sea Lord and Sir Bolton Eyres-Monsell as political head and First Lord. The latter, a *Britannia* product, had joined the Navy in 1894 and, after his marriage in 1904, became an MP in 1910, rejoining the Navy for World War I. In the immediate post war years he had been successively Civil Lord and Financial Secretary just when the Admiralty was beginning to agonise over the Navy's failure to preserve the country from near starvation and to fight and win a Trafalgar. Strongly influenced by his own upbringing he lent his weight to the rising demand for a return to sail training as a means of reinculcating the Nelson spirit and abolishing the Fisher reforms. Chatfield, one of the greatest First Sea Lords to hold that office, with a son at Dartmouth, was markedly less enthusiastic, although he believed that the earlier the 'Darts' and the 'Pubs' from the special (public school) entry, who normally went to HMS *Erebus* for a year (before joining the fleet or going to Keyham for engineering training), were thrown together, the better. So a compromise was reached and HMS *Frobisher* was designated as a training cruiser. To her, instead of HMS *Erebus*, all the special entry cadets were first appointed on joining; and the Darts were also consigned there after 11 terms at Dartmouth,

thus postponing their eagerly anticipated arrival in the fleet for eight
months. But the psychological consequences of this postponement
were never appreciated at the Admiralty. It was enough that the
shadow of sail training had been beaten back.

The Dartmouth curriculum, primitive, sordid and sadistic as it
was, had always been tailored to the moment when the cadet would
join 'the fleet'. Thus in the last year at Dartmouth there was some easing off in the routine and some attempt to make the cadets aware of
the world outside. Once they joined one of HM ships they were, of
course, amongst the lowliest of the low, but in the long run that was
an advantage. Because they were so young, barely 17, and so ignorant, and because most naval ratings were then, as now, kindly indi-
viduals who had gone through training at HMS *Ganges* at least as
tough as Dartmouth, they often covered up for the young officers.
So, although to a very small extent, and depending on the individual,
the cadet might have earned the ratings' respect, the reverse was almost always the case. That was probably the cadet's most important
lesson of all.

The training cruiser, on the other hand, could not differentiate between the Pubs and the Darts and, in the 'interests' of the former,
many of the old absurdities of the early Dartmouth routines were
resurrected. In the fleet the wardroom officers were necessarily a
mixture of the good, the bad and the indifferent; and cadets, if they
kept their eyes and ears open could learn from them all, mainly
through the perceived reactions of the sailors to individual officers,
but in the training cruiser, like Dartmouth and HMS *Erebus*, the officers and most of the petty officers were picked men who, in the case
of the officers, could improve their promotion chances by chasing
the tails off the cadets. There is considerable anecdotal evidence, as
well as evidence of quite senior officers given to the Murray Committee in 1958, that the early days (1933–34) of the training cruiser,
coming on top of the other influences at Dartmouth, caused a degree
of bloody mindedness amongst many Darts with all matters executive. So perhaps here was another 'wind' which blew some Darts of
that particular era, particularly several who had been cadet captains
and chief cadet captains and who were from the intellectually talented 'alpha class', to volunteer for (E) in quite unusual numbers and
despite considerable pressure not to do so. This phenomenon, combined with the increase of 'first choicer' (E)s from the special (public
school) and Pangbourne entries, despite wartime casualties from all

three categories, was to provide (E) officers whose influence on the engineering of the Navy two decades later, in the fields of mobility, weapons and airpower, was to be profound. However, before that, and before they reached their early twenties, they were embroiled in a war for which, in many respects, they soon realised the fleet was ill-prepared.

History suggests that it was the lack of modern aircraft that produced the first shock to the operational capability exercised by the Royal Navy at the beginning of World War II. This was a national and political, rather than an Admiralty scandal. Even the selfless gallantry of the few naval aviators, some of whom also fought so effectively alongside the RAF in the Battle of Britain and later against Rommel's supply line, could not conceal the lack of even moderately modern aircraft to protect the fleet and attack the enemy. The failure to develop and fit the improved anti-aircraft and surface fire control systems that were known to be available, the failure to produce periscopes or rangefinders of a quality remotely comparable to those available to the Germans or later the Japanese, and the primitive 'fall of shot' spotting drills of naval gunnery, continued to cost lives and ships throughout the war. These were all parts of the same picture of a Navy that had lagged technologically during the locust years. Young officers, as well as their seniors, started to question why this was so.

The most critical and immediate shock to the operational effectiveness of the British fleet was its lack of true mobility. Reference has already been made to Fisher's recommendation that fuelling at sea was essential, and how this was wholly ignored, and to his assertion that the Navy should never tie itself only to one fuel, which is exactly what the Engineer in Chief and the Admiralty Fuel Experimental Station (AFES) did. Provided the premier grade Persian fuel remained in Admiralty storages all was well, but very soon in the Atlantic battle the only fuels available, containing very different constituents to Persian fuels, came from the Caribbean or North America; and the operational penalty was disastrous. In pre-radar days smoke was the 'give-away' and and when Caribbean fuels were squirted into the furnaces with AFES sprayers designed for Persian fuels, smoke was often inevitable. These problems are explained in detail later. What is relevant here is that none of the many materiel problems nor the untold hours of labour from men weary from days at sea or battle that each involved, had ever been foreseen as they should have been during the easy going years of peace. 'To prepare for war is one of the most effective ways of preserving peace', George Washington is reputed to have said. There were no George Washingtons in the hierarchy of the Engineer in Chief's department during the locust years, and the naval staff were fully engaged in abolishing, or at least reducing, the impact of technology and the influence of its naval engineering acolytes, rather than in finding ways to use it to improve warfighting effectiveness.

Captain, later Vice Admiral (E) Sir Denys Ford, the first Fisher trained (E) officer later to become Engineer in Chief of the Fleet, thus stressing for the first time his unique responsibility for mobility, was the Fleet Engineer Officer, Home Fleet, when the country went to war. Conscious in his office in the flagship at Scapa of the appalling ordeals young engineers were facing to keep their ships, large or small, operational, he launched volleys of letters towards his parent department, as well as at the Director of Naval Construction and Director of Electrical Engineering, all in Bath, on matters affecting their departments. From the Engineer in Chief he demanded answers to five main questions.

Why had arrangements never been made to fuel ships at sea?

Who was responsible for condemning the fleet to operate effectively only on Persian fuel?

Why was British steam pipe jointing material so poor?

What arrangements were contemplated to enhance evaporator capacity which was well below that so obviously essential?

Could not the 21 day boiler cleaning rule be relaxed?

The responses he received were almost entirely unhelpful, although the boiler cleaning period was grudgingly extended to 750 hours instead of the 21 'days'. Some of his queries were answered in a practical way, when the first of the US navy 'four stackers' (of the destroyers for bases deal) appeared in the UK. Their steam jointing material was superior to that in use in the Royal Navy so that, aged as they were, steam leaks were the exception and not the rule and thus boiler water consumption was less, easing the load on the evaporators.

The USN used chemical treatment comparable to that used in the British power station industry to prevent corrosion, to the extent that their boilers could be steamed for 2000 hours before the onerous task of boiler cleaning became necessary; and the same chemical when injected into evaporators greatly eased the evaporator maintenance load.

To these priceless bits of information Bath remained resolutely deaf; while to the submissions by Ford and others, pointing out their relevance to improved serviceability in a hard pressed fleet, Bath was unconquerably mute.

A close friend of Captain Ford, Captain (E) C H Nicholson (who, as mentioned earlier had had much to do with changing the outlook on engineering at Dartmouth) became the extra naval assistant to the Second Sea Lord for engineering personnel (EAP) responsible in practical terms for the appointing of all types of engineering officer: old type (pre-Fisher) engineers; (E) officers; warrant engineers and mechanicians; RNVR and RNR engineers and so on. On him fell the heavy task of spreading the seagoing engineering talent that remained from the officer casualty list sustained in the first two years of the war, into posts where they could most contribute by their experience to the long war he and Ford foresaw. Apprised by Ford of the difficulties under which the fleet was suffering, Nicholson took the difficult decision to feed in many war experienced officers to the department of the Engineer in Chief, regardless of the fact that this would mean the removal of the long serving and very design experienced officers (some of whom were anxious to get to sea anyway), as well as into the dockyard staffs and the teaching staff at Keyham, where young engineer officers were being trained, and to the newly established damage control school in London. Ford and Nicholson hoped that these officers, many of them survivors, all of them battle experienced, would be the harbingers of some sort of engineering revolution. With luck such revolutionaries might trigger a fundamental change in the prevailing habits of thought in machinery design and operating practice, in line with the best in British and American industry, to the ultimate improvement of mobility and the better wartime operational serviceability of the Royal Navy.

Chapter 7
Full Steam Ahead
1942–1950

No difficulty baffles great zeal

Memories
Admiral of the Fleet Lord Fisher

Despite the apparent pre-war inertia in the department of the Engineer in Chief, a critical decision had been taken which was to provide the power house of the forthcoming engineering revolution. Two 'specialist' sections, one studying boiler design and one turbine and gearing design, were created quite separate from the existing ship type sections. Each consisted of high quality 'dagger' officers and the boiler section was empowered to give direction to the Admiralty Fuel Experimental Station (AFES) on investigations into practical fleet problems, rather than following deep studies which were often less likely to produce useful operational dividends, as was the wont of the apt to be autonomous AFES.

The second section, similarly manned, was directed to look at the present and future policy regarding naval steam turbine propulsion, with particular reference to improvements in overall efficiency which might give ships greater range for a given amount of fuel. They were also to be responsible for the study of gearing as greater efficiency was bound to require higher speed turbines and therefore possibly double-reduction gearing between the turbines and the comparatively slow moving propeller. Over the next few years of war and subsequent peace these two sections were mainly responsible for giving the fleet the improved mobility it so desperately needed.

On the outbreak of war the personnel of the Engineer in Chief's department mustered on platform number four at Paddington station, each with a suitcase and a slide rule, and embarked a Great Western train for an unknown destination. As the train drew out, the Engineer in Chief, in the uniform of an Engineer Vice Admiral, staying in London and at Paddington only to say farewell, stood at salute

The Engineer in Chief's department leaving Paddington, September 1939 (photograph courtesy Mr Sampson).

with what has been described as a 'Casabianca' look on his face. In due course his faithful acolytes, under the command of his deputy, fetched up at The Spa Hotel in Bath. In Bath they still remain. This move presented immense bureaucratic upheaval, especially as the shipbuilding tempo consequent on the preparations for war, had already caused a monumental increase in work load; soon to be further enhanced by the onerous duties and perils confronting the civilian staff on Home Guard duties. It fell to a senior draughtsman to be the first (but not, so history relates, the last) inadvertently to discharge his musket through the ceiling into the office of the deputy engineer in chief on the floor above.

Little has been written about the work during the war of the 'extra naval assistant to the Second Sea Lord for engineering personnel' (EAP) mentioned in chapter 5. In the early days, when casualties of engineer officers soared and throughout the blitz, it was Captain (E) later Rear-Admiral (E) C H Nicholson CB, from his London office who kept a cool head, who telephoned the next of kin of officer survivors and who insisted on a policy of rotating engineer officers from sea to shore and back again so that war experience was constantly injected into the design, training and dockyard departments. His was no easy task, but it was carried out with consummate skill against enormous odds and to a great extent was the driving force behind the engineering revolution that Nicholson and Captain Ford saw was needed.

One of the first of what were sometimes called 'Nicholson's revolutionaries' (although the officer in question prefers to be called an innovator), was Lieutenant-Commander (E) Leonard Baker; and he was appointed to the Boiler Section. Baker was a hockey player of inter-service distinction and probably the first (E) officer to be decorated with the Distinguished Service Cross, awarded for his efforts in helping to bring a badly bombed and near sinking HMS *Suffolk* from Narvik to Glasgow.

While Baker worked himself into his new appointment he fed many ideas to the AFES so that modifications were made to naval boilers to give them a higher forcing rate (produce more steam for a given amount of fuel burnt; and therefore improved miles per gallon). With Lieutenant Commander (E) Cooper (at the AFES) he also modified the fuel burning equipment to overcome the operationally dangerous effects (smoke) of burning Western hemisphere fuel. When the US Navy 'four stackers' arrived the merits of chemical treatment of boiler water to prevent internal boiler corrosion became plain. Baker, aware that the electricity industry had been successfully using chemical treatment for years pressed hard for trials, preparatory to the introduction of the chemical known as US navy boiler compound throughout the British fleet. But the hierarchy in the Engineer in Chief's department were unimpressed, although they rather stuffily conceded that the ex-USN (now British) ships could continue to use it. Indeed so remote was Bath from the war that Baker's appeals, and Captain Ford's demands from Scapa Flow, were met with the answer that the more frequent (750 hour) (British) period between cleaning boilers (rather than the 2000 hour period now clearly possible), carried out by artificers and stokers, arguably the hardest worked element of any ship's company, was necessary to give the remainder of the crew an essential rest. This at a moment in our history when the country was desperately short of warships of all sorts and the need for operational serviceability was paramount!

Frustrated, Baker induced the appointers to send him back to sea as soon as a suitable vacancy occurred. Thus he relieved the officer who had established the boiler section, Lieutenant-Commander (E) E G Williams, by then Senior Engineer of HMS *Victorious*. They had kept in touch and, when *Victorious* was in the States refitting, Williams had laid in a large stock of US boiler compound. Aware of Bath's objections he did not use it in the boilers but in the evaporators, where its benign labour saving effect by making the hard salt encrustation on the heating coils so much easier to remove (always by hand), was at once apparent. On taking over Williams' appointment as Senior Engineer, Baker informed his Chief, Commander, later Captain (E) Basil Cronk DSC, of the positive merits of this chemical treatment and Cronk told their Captain, later Admiral Sir Michael Denny, GCB, CBE, DSO. Between them, and in the full knowledge that it was against direct written orders from Bath, they decided to conduct a carefully monitored trial as soon as *Victorious* returned safely from an operation to bomb Stavanger. This trial, fully documented, the insides of the boiler drums photographed and scrupulously examined, took place as *Victorious* sailed from Scapa to Sydney, Australia. The results were incontrovertible. The internal state of the boilers steamed on boiler compound was better after 750 hours than the boilers which had not yet used it; and 2000 hours steaming showed that the internal state was still entirely satisfactory.

During the *Victorious* voyage Baker could do little to improve the poor evaporator capacity, which damaged morale by the rationing of washing water (except, as already mentioned, to use US boiler compound which reduced the work load when the heating coils had to be descaled), so he addressed himself, with the help of Bombay dockyard, to changing the whole messdeck ventilation system of the ship. His theory, that there should be a low velocity stream of air throughout, instead of the high velocity and ineffective punkah louvres much beloved of the naval constructors, was confirmed. The very real improvement in habitability that he achieved was of great benefit to the ship's company and morale was improved. On arrival in Australia, Denny, now fully convinced by the technical judgements of Cronk and Baker, reported the results of the boiler trial to Admiral Sir Philip Vian, commanding the aircraft carriers. Vian and Admiral Sir Bernard Rawlings commanding the battleships, were probably the two most battle experienced British admirals of the war; and they both well understood that without maximum mobility the fleet was impotent. Their influence therefore prevailed over the explicitly repeated instructions from the Admiralty, and US navy boiler compound was ordered to be used in all ships of the British Pacific Fleet (BPF). Had this not been the case then the BPF could not have played its part, small though it may have been compared to the US navy, in the greatest maritime campaign in history.

The rest of the Baker story is a sad one as far as the Royal Navy is concerned. Baker was promoted on the very strong recommendations of Admiral Vian and the Fleet Engineer officer, but on his return to the UK he was threatened with court-martial for flagrant and deliberate disobedience of orders. However the Head of the Naval Law division sagely pointed out that Cronk and Denny would have to stand beside Baker in the dock, and the number of defendants could hardly stop there! So, despite pressure from senior engineering officers in the Admiralty, the Board refused to agree to disciplinary proceedings. Baker's services to the Navy were not yet at an end as will be recounted later.

The problems arising from the very close and cosy association of the Engineer in Chief's elite coterie with the shipbuilding industry were described in chapter 5 and these the newly created 'turbine and gearing section' set out to remove as soon as two prime revolutionaries from sea arrived. Commander later Rear-Admiral (E) I G Maclean, CB, OBE, from HMS *Renown* was in charge and was joined by Lieutenant (E) later Vice Admiral Sir George Raper KCB, fresh from Russian convoy battles and the sinking of HMS *Edinburgh*, where his bravery and leadership had earned him a year's accelerated advancement and a mention in despatches. Both were determined to alter the whole pattern of naval machinery design and production. In this endeavour they were fortunate that in the new section there was already one of the many skilled and far sighted engineering draughtsmen common within the department. Mr Norton's name will always stand high in the history of those days.

Captain (E) Denys Ford and his successor as Fleet Engineer Officer, Home Fleet, Captain (E) the Hon Denis Maxwell, were the

mouthpieces of the many at sea who realised how far ahead the
Americans were in achieving true mobility. Boiler cleaning apart, it
became clear during operations in the Atlantic that the USN could
stay at sea for much longer periods than the RN. In terms of efficient
machinery, making for economical use of fuel (miles per gallon—or
ton), minimum weight and space occupied by machinery and boilers, and therefore more room for fuel and weapons, and even in the
work load to keep the ships operational, the US navy was light years
ahead of the RN. This superiority was not confined to those ships
built with such speed and regardless of expense after the Pearl Harbour disaster. To the present generation of British naval engineers all
this would come as no surprise. To those trained between the wars it
was a matter for astonishment and shame.

Three challenges faced the younger and more battle experienced
(E) officers sent to the Engineer in Chief's department in Bath. The
first was to modify those ships destined for the Pacific as quickly and
as thoroughly as human ingenuity and the resources available in a
war torn Britain would permit. In practice this meant installing more
evaporator capacity wherever feasible to produce more boiler and
drinking water, in improving machinery space ventilation to make
life 'below' less intolerable, in stirring the naval constructors to bring
messdeck ventilation arrangements to a more acceptable level of
habitability, and to fit as many domestic refrigerators and drinking
water coolers as could be procured from a war oriented British industry or brought over in warships refitted in the United States.
Lastly, with the Director of Electrical Engineering, it was necessary
to supply and fit emergency diesel generators to all those ships
which lacked this essential damage control feature. Beyond this any
further improvement in the war fighting capability of the British
ships going to the Pacific had to be left to the leadership and technical
expertise of what remained of the whole pre-war (E) branch, from
commanders (E) and engineer-commanders, to long service artificers and mechanicians and stokers; massively diluted as the
whole branch now was with willing but inexperienced RNVR (E) officers and hostilities only (HO) ratings.

The second task for the 'revolutionaries' was to initiate measures
to ensure that the Royal Navy of the future would enjoy a mobility at
least as good as, and if possible better than, that common in the US
navy, and to achieve this before the economies of peace intervened.
The third task, with the help of the more senior Fisher scheme offi-

cers now moving towards the top, was to overcome the less amena-
ble reactionaries in Bath and to establish a much closer liaison with
the naval staff. Without a common and united front in the Admiralty, the shipbuilders and their marine engineering elements would
certainly never be coaxed into a more forward looking attitude, nor
would the money be forthcoming. So Maclean, Raper and Norton
started to formulate a more adventurous policy for the future and
'sell it' to the naval staff, as well as to their hidebound engineering
seniors and to the shipbuilders.

Maclean's team uncovered the fact that the US navy had suffered
from the Parsons steam turbine manufacturing licence arrangements as had the RN, but rather than sit tight and do nothing the
USN had managed to overcome intense lobbying in Congress and
abolish Parsons turbines. Instead they stated their requirements for
boilers and turbines and place contracts with whatever power station firms came up with potentially satisfactory answers. This policy
was of benefit in two ways. Since several firms were concerned there
was an element of competition, and, accepting that power station
technology would always be ahead of the more testing and space reduced conditions at sea, there would be plenty of experience available when considering the suitability of any design for fitting in
warships.

Clearly the first hurdle was Maclean's seniors in Bath and the
next the shipbuilders' habits and attitudes. It was still anticipated
that the Pacific war, with the vast distances to be steamed away from
base support, would last for several years and a class of destroyers
was under construction specifically for service in that campaign. By
now the difference in the mobility of the respective fleets might have
seemed obvious, but Maclean's argument that the new Daring class
must be able to operate on level terms with the US navy in the Pacific
was not fully accepted, at least at first. Here the reactionary Bath
pundits and the shipbuilders found an unexpected ally, though for a
different reason, in the First Sea Lord. Admiral Sir Andrew Cunningham, despite all the immense courage and leadership he displayed
in the geographically restricted Mediterranean, never really appreciated that what he saw as the abnormal conditions in the Pacific, were
in reality the operational conditions which any navy purporting to
be ocean going should be able to meet. Also Cunningham was never
such an admirer of American naval capability and habits as Admiral
Sir Bruce Fraser was soon to become. Later, Cunningham rather

changed his view, for he was to write, '...in cruisers and destroyers there was in my opinion a grave tendency to sacrifice fighting power for endurance...destroyers were too large and had become carriers of radar and radar ratings...', he later continued, '...in justice, it must be said that the destroyers were good ships for the abnormal sort of war being fought in the Pacific'.

With his infectious enthusiasm, and the drawings and data given him by the Chief of the Bureau of Ships in Washington DC, Maclean managed to convince executive allies on the naval staff that he was on the right lines and they moved matters forward.

With some finesse Maclean proposed that the shipbuilders, who with all their faults were patriots, should form a committee and, having been shown the operational requirements of the Pacific war and the various pieces of British and American technical data laid before them, should recommend to the Engineer in Chief how the Daring class destroyers should be boilered and engined. With this carrot Maclean let it be known that there was a stick in the background, in the shape of carefully checked evidence recording the Navy's dissatisfaction with the long list of shipbuilders' shortcomings.

Maclean and Raper were about 90% successful. The Bath hierarchy conceded and the committee agreed that the advanced steam conditions then prevailing in the British power station industry were suitable for the new Daring class. It was decided that they should be boilered by Babcock and Foster Wheeler, both of whose USA counterparts were already suppliers to the US navy.

The committee of shipbuilders too, like Maclean, were clever 'operators'. They cunningly proposed to the Engineer in Chief (perhaps himself less convinced than Maclean and Raper of the merits of the new policy) that the shipbuilders should combine together and take over the Parson's licence with a new organisation to be called Parson's and Marine Engineer's Turbine and Research and Design Association (PAMETRADA). This association, they proposed, would design turbines for the shipbuilders to manufacture, would carry out research and would set up the boiler and turbine test house for which (after a strongly worded memorandum by Maclean) approval had now been received from the Treasury. To this arrangement the Engineer in Chief agreed, as well as supporting the idea that PAMETRADA designed turbines should be fitted to the Daring class destined for the Pacific. Maclean, still sceptical of the PAMETRADA arrangement, managed to have inserted an important and far seeing clause permitting the Admiralty to obtain turbines from the best in British industry, once PAMETRADA had established itself.

The shipbuilders' committee meanwhile had realised that the English Electric Advanced Propulsion Machinery Design was already worthy of consideration. Sir Harold Yarrow (the son of Sir Alfred Yarrow with whom Fisher had been so friendly) therefore broke ranks from the shipbuilders' caucus and, with Maclean's blessing, undertook at once to fit these (non-PAMETRADA) English Electric turbines in the two Daring class destroyers being built in his yard at Scotstoun. This action helped overcome another technical hurdle. Very high speed turbines, giving the much needed greater efficiency, had to use double reduction gearing to bring down the driving shaft and propeller speed. At that time such gearing sets were not manufactured in the UK, although common in the USA. However Switzerland had gear cutting machines of great accuracy and as the European war was now over and dollars were short, Yarrow had the double reduction gearing for his two ships manufactured in Switzerland.

Maclean and his team and other similar 'revolutionaries' at Bath managed to move mountains, but as they reached one summit it became clear there were further peaks to climb. If the momentum was to be kept up, reinforcements were necessary, and with peace in the air there was little hope of extra naval help. Maclean therefore, on behalf of the Admiralty, contracted with Sir Harold Yarrow and English Electric, who were working so well together, to make a world survey of power station, merchant ship and naval machinery. From the results the combined team was asked to propose the best machinery for a given set of destroyer design parameters, and for a far more advanced design likely to be suitable for the future.

Then, quite suddenly, the naval staff had a long hoped for brainstorm. Now, like Bath, full of people with recent war experience, they set Maclean a daunting challenge by putting together an urgent staff requirement for an escort frigate that could cross the Atlantic without refuelling, and with a 25–30% reduction in weight and space occupied by machinery and fuel. Mobility had come home to roost and with it Admiral Cunningham's requirement for more weaponry too.

Clearly this 'great leap forward' was a task for the newly created Yarrow/English Electric team who, by then, were well on the way to assembling a comprehensive corpus of worldwide knowledge and experience. There was a snag. English Electric, at the time the ac-knowledged foremost turbine designers in the country, with the great (later Lord) Willis Jackson FRS as their research director, wished to compete for the order, so clearly could not be part of the team drawing up the specification. Thus, not for the first time in its long and famous history, the firm of Yarrows once more came to the Admiralty's rescue, putting patriotism before any thought of profit. Sir Harold Yarrow relinquished the right his firm had had for half a century to tender for boilers or other machinery of Yarrow manufac-ture, and agreed with Maclean and the Engineer in Chief to set up the Yarrow-Admiralty Research Department (Y-ARD). This was to be a semi-autonomous organisation which worked for the Admiralty and industry on a fee charging basis with the Admiralty work al-ways having priority. From this small beginning Y-ARD (today known simply as YARD) has been, and still is, of immense value to the Navy, to the Merchant Navy and fishing industries, and to Brit-ain's export drive. Mr E Norton, later honoured with the CBE, the draughtsman who had helped Maclean and Raper to set the steam revolution in motion, was permitted to leave the naval service and, with the enthusiastic backing of the Engineer in Chief and Sir Harold Yarrow soon became Managing Director of Yarrows and Vice Chair-

Mr E Norton. Engineering draughtsman in the department of the Engineer in Chief, closely involved with the 'revolutions' of Maclean and Raper (photograph courtesy YARD).

man of YARD thus providing an invaluable link with Headquarters at Bath as well as additional resources whenever needed.

All this effort at Bath, and particularly within YARD, led to the installation of what was called the Y 100 and Y 101 sets of steam machinery, far in advance of anything hitherto developed in terms of efficiency, space occupied and ease of maintenance. This machinery was installed finally in over 110 frigates or similar warships of 8 different navies. Fifty-six sets were in RN frigates of which several were in action in the Falklands, as were HMS *Fearless* and *Intrepid* the assault ships, also with Y 100 machinery.

In the immediate aftermath of the war, by which time Ford was deputy engineer in chief and Engineer in Chief of the Fleet (designate), he and Nicholson, by now a Rear-Admiral but still in charge of engineer officer's appointing, carried out a reshuffle of senior (E) 'chairs'. The old guard were due to go; and they went. By appointing, engineering specialists from the Navy's air world, from the dockyards, from ordnance engineering and yet others with a submarine background, as assistant engineers in chief, as well as officers with great marine engineering experience, Nicholson brought successful and war experienced men of widely differing professional engineering experience together to apply their ideas and expertise to the improvement of all aspects of fleet mobility, to the professional training of (E) officers and to the future training pattern for ratings of all engineering disciplines.

It was these officers and their widely experienced juniors who saw that, just as sail had given way to steam in the nineteenth century, advancing technology was providing other means of propulsion which one day might succeed steam and give the Navy the mobility it had so painfully lacked in World War II.

Chapter 8
Anything but Steam
1942–1960

Vickers are absolutely confident they can produce a 25 knot Dread-
nought equal to any building or projected ship and capable of going
round the world without refuelling. They are prepared to go nap on it
with 68,000 horsepower on four shafts. Oram and the Admiralty are
timorous—of course they are! They were timorous with the water-
tube boiler! They were timorous at the turbine going into the Dread-
nought! We've got to push them over the precipice! Half a loaf is
better than no bread. They strain at the gnat of perfection and swal-
low the camel of the unready. What breaks my heart is that you can't
see your way to associate the turbine with the principle of internal
combustion propulsion.* Isn't there some metal that will stand the
heat? Dr Beilby will invent it for you. Can't you see the way to some
experiment ?

Letter from Admiral of the Fleet Lord Fisher to
Sir Charles Parsons, Oct 14th,1912

Mention has already been made of the lack of diesel expertise outside the submarine service in the Royal Navy in the 1920s and 1930s.
Even diesels in ships' boats were not as common as might be expected, although several different makes were in use. World War II
changed all that. By the end of the war the Admiralty had more than
300 types of internal combustion engines in use, and the refitting and
spare part situation was chaotic. Experience in the other services was
similar, though not quite on the same awe inspiring scale. It fell to the
Admiralty to suggest a committee to standardize on various ranges
of engines from one horsepower up to 2000 horsepower or more.

This policy decision was the begetter of the Admiralty standard
range diesel engine (ASR) which could be assembled in line or in a
'V' formation depending on the horsepower and the particular service required. After development the 'V' turbo-supercharged ASR 1
engine had a twenty four hour rating at over 2,200 horsepower.

* The first known mention of a gas turbine

The Admiralty Engineering Laboratory (AEL) at West Drayton, like the other elements of the (E) branch, benefited in 1943 from Captain Nicholson's appointing policy. Commander (E) C M Hall, a submarine and diesel specialist before his promotion to commander, had been for sometime the Chief of the (steam driven) HMS *Aurora*, successfully operating against Rommels's supply lines and sinking some 120,000 tons of enemy shipping. Now given the acting rank of Captain (E) and appointed Superintendent of the AEL, he was once more in his favourite professional element. From the AEL he produced a number of valuable initiatives from which much has evolved.

First came two astonishing coincidences. A Mr Sammons, the managing director of a small engineering firm in Slough asked Hall at AEL to type test one of his engines at double the designed revolutions, and this engine proved exactly suitable for small high speed naval motor boats. This favour brought them together and they became friends. One day Mr Sammons reported to Captain Hall that he had received from the Middle East a case marked 'secret', and was in considerable doubt, in view of this security classification, as to what he should do with it. His contacts in the Air Ministry denied all knowledge and he was hesitant as to whether he should open it. Captain Hall was unworried by any such inhibition. On opening it, Hall and Sammons found it to contain an unused German Junkers Jumo diesel engine. Hall at once volunteered to type test this booty and, like much German designed machinery, it proved to be a brilliant concept. It was during the analysing of the various readings that one of the Engineer in Chief's many great draughtsmen, Mr H Penwarden, suggested that the engine might well be developed into three 'banks', in a very compact 'delta' shape. If this proved practical then the result seemed likely to produce 2,500 horsepower.

After development at the AEL the Deltic, as the engine came to be called, was added to the five or six engines under examination by Sir Roy Fedden's committee as a possibility for Coastal Forces. When, finally, the Deltic was chosen to power the MTBs and MGBs, Mr Sammons became chief engineer of Napiers, the firm selected to contract for the Deltic's further development and up-rating. The Deltic could not, of course, be refitted in the cramped engine rooms of coastal craft, but required a proper workshop. However, ease of access into coastal craft ensured a rapid exchange of engines and so 'refit by replacement', as is normal in the aircraft industry, made its way

The Deltic engine, developed by the admiralty engineering laboratory at West Drayton, following the unexplained delivery of the German Junkers Jumo diesel engine. Use of the Deltic in coastal craft brought refit by replacement into the Navy as standard practice (photograph courtesy YARD).

into the Navy, where 'refit by repair' had usually been the rule. The operational readiness of coastal craft was greatly improved.

When the post-war reductions led to the virtual disappearance of the Coastal Forces fleet, British Rail turned to the Deltic for a considerable period. Today, in a modified form, it is still in use in some of the Navy's latest minesweepers.

Strangely, at least until the last few years, the RAF, like the Navy, have been very conservative within their own service in their relationship with engineering and engineers. This is not the place to record the difficult path that Squadron Leader (later Air Commodore Sir) Frank Whittle had to tread from 1930 until the end of the war when, rather later than Germany, his jet engines were at last fitted in British aircraft. Once the development of jet engines started however, though so far as can be discovered without any recollection of Fisher's proposals 34 years before, the Navy became interested in the maritime possibilities of gas turbines.

The constant problem facing naval marine engineers has been that the comparatively small number of high horsepower steam propulsion units involved has militated against shore development testing. The development costs, unlike those of more numerous aircraft engines, could simply never be spread amongst the comparatively few marine production runs. There were therefore profound economic reasons for somehow tying the Navy to the rapidly developing aircraft engine industry. But the practical difficulties to be overcome seemed formidable.

Gas turbines are necessarily high speed engines whereas marine propellers are slow moving in a dense medium. Ships have to be able to go astern, which implies serious gearing or variable pitch propeller problems. Steam turbines can have an astern turbine incorporated; gas turbines cannot. A gas turbine requires a vast and concentrated volume of air for combustion, and the design of the necessarily large air intakes is crucial if surging is to be prevented and smooth running ensured, while air intakes have also to be designed with the need for whole engines to be passed down them when engine exchange becomes necessary. Yet these intakes must not prove a flooding hazard should the ship be damaged in action. It was cross flooding through the funnel uptakes that finally caused the aircraft carrier HMS *Ark Royal* to sink in World War II. This was a design problem which the Royal Corps of Naval Constructors (RCNC) tackled and overcame with their usual flair. Seaborne gas turbines were also likely, unless strict precautions were taken, to ingest salt laden air or actual sea water. Salt and high temperature ferrous metals are always hostile bed fellows. This too presented a serious problem and kerosene, bran, canary seed, ground walnut husks, wheatings and various emulsions were injected with the air at one time or another, either to blast off or wash the salt from the turbine blades, before a more satisfactory air intake, siting and effective filtration, solved this very real difficulty.

Lastly there was a serious fuel problem. Aircraft fuel, in those days normally used in gas turbines, was carried in carefully designed tanks in the wings of aircraft. Warship fuel was necessarily stowed in all sorts of out of the way compartments around the ship. Normal aircraft fuel, with comparatively high volatility, thus stored, would constitute a fire and explosion risk, so less volatile fuels, still acceptable by gas turbines would be needed; and during the twenty years or more that it might take to change the Navy from steam to gas turbine propulsion the fleet would either have to be supplied with two sorts of fuel, an almost impossible and expensive logistic nightmare, or fuels acceptable to both boilers and gas turbines would have to be found. This difficulty too, as will be related later, was finally solved.

When Hall arrived at the AEL the application of gas turbines to marine propulsion was in its early stages in the form of what was called the Fratric free piston/gas turbine development. The free piston element was eventually abandoned, but the gas turbine element went on to be developed by Metropolitan-Vickers. This development and Hall's acknowledged brilliance ensured his co-option onto the powerful gas turbine collaboration committee, an association of the chief engineers of Rolls-Royce, Metropolitan-Vickers, Bristols, Armstrong-Siddeley, Power Jets (Whittle) and the National Gas Turbine Establishment, together with other engineers and experts in fuel technology. The outstanding chairman of this bunch of some of Britain's greatest engineers was Dr Roxbee Cox, afterwards Lord Kings Norton.

Later Hall, who like Baker had ruffled the calm waters of the Engineer in Chief's hierachy by his insistence on the future of gas turbines and by his development of a captured Jumo into a very promising Deltic, a type of Diesel seen by some as a potential rival to the Admiralty developed ASR 1, reverted in rank once more to commander (E) and took charge of the newly formed gas turbine section in his parent department at Bath. Here, presumably, it was thought he might be more controllable than at West Drayton. From Bath Hall was able to organise the prolonged development running (because of the noise in a disused salt mine) of the Metropolitan-Vickers Gatric marine gas turbine. After proving itself, this engine was installed in HM Motor Gunboat 2009. This was the first warship ever to be propelled by a gas turbine, although there was still a Packard diesel as a standby.

By now the developments in steam propulsion directed by Maclean and Raper were occupying the attention of many of the best brains in the slowly evolving 'new look' Engineer in Chief's department. Understandably there was a degree of professional tension between the 'high pressure, high temperature steam brigade' and the (initially regarded as rather upstart) gas turbine and diesel proponents of mobility. This was good for all. The hierachy were now at last beginning to understand, under Maclean's prodding, that the mobility of the fleet for which they alone were responsible had, in the past, degenerated into a blunt weapon and that the future lay in

HM Motor Gunboat 2009, the first warship to be propelled by gas turbine, although a Packard standby was also fitted (photograph courtesy Lt Cmdr Maber).

steam. They found it hard to stomach Hall's prophecy on a docket in the late 1940s that, within twenty years, the Navy would be dependent on gas turbines alone for its mobility. In fact it took a bit more than that because Britain was leading the world and there were no short cuts. The first major all gas turbine warship went to sea about 25 years after Hall wrote his memorandum.

The Navy lost Kit Hall to industry and he was succeeded by Leonard Baker, no longer threatened with court martial. Baker, despite his steam expertise, entirely shared Hall's view of the future, but when he failed to persuade the Treasury to allocate funds already voted that year for gas turbine development, he too retired. The Blue Funnel Line acquired a great Marine Superintendent.

Although the Navy has lost two revolutionaries, Baker and Hall, whose legacies it still enjoys, the continued appointment of high calibre professional war-experienced (E) officers ensured that, despite high wartime casualties, there were always others in the (E) branch all equally capable professionally, and with a broad outlook, who were available to step into their shoes. Commander (E) later Rear-Admiral H G H Tracy CB DSC, destined to be the Director of Marine Engineering when the gas turbine finally proved itself at sea, was succeeded in charge of the gas turbine section by Commander

(E) later Vice Admiral Sir Allan Trewby KCB, later a member of the Board of Admiralty. Soon after there came Commander (E) later Rear-Admiral L D Dymoke CB, like Tracy another Pangbourne graduate. Dymoke, at an earlier and critical moment in 1948 had been attached to Rolls-Royce in Derby to guide the firm in the development of the RM 60 Rolls Royce gas turbine, which eventually went to sea in HM Gunboat *Grey Goose*. This was the first warship in the world to be propelled solely by gas turbine as there was no form of standby power plant. Besides leading the gas turbine section, Dymoke later led the successful engineering team which provided the nuclear propulsion plants for Britain's Polaris submarines.

These two parallel advances in naval warship propulsion implied changes in rating and, indeed, officer training. Fisher's artificer and mechanician training early this century had emphasised the practical skills of craftsmanship then needed for the wide variety of steam machinery and for diesels, there was now a new requirement to introduce a deeper understanding of marine engineering theory, so as to make available the knowledge necessary for the maintenance and operation of gas turbines, high speed diesels and, eventually, nuclear machinery. In turn this meant higher rating entry standards and a more advanced training syllabus for all ranks and

HM Gunboat *Grey Goose*, the first warship to be propelled solely by gas turbine (photograph courtesy Lt Cmdr Maber).

ratings concerned with naval engineering, as it related to propulsion and mobility. Both Tracy and Trewby at different times headed the professional engineering training of all (E) officers at the new Royal Naval Engineering College (RNEC) at Manadon. There, in conjunction with their Instructor Branch colleagues, they and Captain W B S Milln, also at one time in charge of marine engineering training and later Captain at RNEC, did much to raise the professional standards of the young (E) officers who would have to carry the 'revolutionary' torch in the future in the marine, as well as in the air and weapon environments.

Tracy, Raper, Haynes (mentioned later), Trewby and Dymoke were also all in command at one time or another in those critical years, of HMS *Sultan*, then the mechanicians' training school at Gosport, and of HMS *Caledonia* at Rosyth and HMS *Fisgard* at Torpoint, the two artificers' training establishments. Between them they radically changed rating training to meet the needs of the technological future.

Advances in steam propulsion as an aid to improved fleet mobility were dealt with in chapter 7. This chapter has so far dealt with the moves forward in diesel and gas turbine propulsion. It remains to mention two other mobility options that were being pursued simultaneously. These were hydrogen peroxide propulsion for submarines and nuclear propulsion for submarines and surface ships.

Hydrogen peroxide had a dramatic start but a short innings. A team consisting of Commander (E) later Rear-Admiral I G Aylen CB, DSC, another war experienced 'dagger' officer who also contributed greatly to the professional expertise of the whole (E) branch as Captain of Manadon and assistant engineer in chief (personnel) when the new college was under construction, Commander (E) C M Hall from AEL (already mentioned) and Commander (E) later Rear-Admiral W A Haynes CB, Director-General, dockyards, were following Field Marshal Montgomery and the British and Canadian armies into Germany. Dr Walther, the inventor of the 'V' rockets and other weapons had turned his fertile brain to high speed submarine propulsion with the dangerously inflammable hydrogen peroxide as fuel. This was one of the developments the team was seeking out.

Aylen's team found three such submarines almost operationally ready, with speeds greater than allied anti-submarine vessels and so potentially lethal weapons, had the war not ended when it did. One submarine had gone aground in the prevailing chaos of surrender

HM Submarine Explorer *at high speed on the surface.* Explorer *was believed to be the fastest submarine in the world at that time (photograph courtesy IWM).*

and was at once allocated to the Russians. The second, when Hall was inspecting it, was (probably inadvertently) set on fire by a German artificer and this boat the British allocated to the Americans. The third submarine, with the then unheard of underwater operational speed of 30 knots, was dispatched to Vickers at Barrow in Furness. Vickers built two facsimiles for the Navy, HM S/Ms *Explorer* and *Excalibur* which, for a time, were used by brave crews as rather perilous underwater high speed target vessels. Thus was the Navy made aware of the speeds that would be common once nuclear submarines became part of a British or enemy fleet and so tactical doctrines could start development.

The need for nuclear power for both surface and submarine propulsion was recognised very soon after the war by the Engineer in Chief, and a team of (E) propulsion specialists were brought together at the Atomic Energy Research Establishment (AERE) at Harwell under Captain (E) S A Harrison-Smith CBE. As a result of their skill and labour, Captain (E) N J H D'Arcy with Commander (E), later Rear-Admiral W T C Ridley CB were dispatched to the United States to discuss with the USN mutual plans for the development of an 'atomic boiler'. Admiral Hyman G Rickover USN, already well on the way with his own designs for submarine and surface nuclear propulsion, repulsed the team, who returned with the very secret folio of plans unopened. Unfortunately, the British government of the day ruled that the development of nuclear power for electricity generation should take precedence over nuclear propulsion for either warships or sea borne transport. This lack of appreciation of the possibilities of nuclear power by politicians in those now far off days is unsurprising when it is common knowledge that a recent Secretary of State for Defence, after some time in office, expressed amazement that nuclear propulsion also involved the use of steam! Sadly there are few engineers in Parliament. So in the end, and despite the progress initially made by the Navy at Harwell, a later government had to go cap in hand to the United States and ask Admiral Rickover USN for help with HM S/M *Dreadnought*, Britain's first nuclear propelled submarine, then having its (largely American) machinery and nuclear reactors installed under Captain Ridley's brilliant supervision.

With hindsight the Navy was exceptionally well served technologically in the 1940s and 1950s. Under the drive of the engineering officers already referred to, and with the sympathy and help of a naval staff becoming more technologically minded than ever before, the 'mobility revolution' had produced several options. Maclean and Raper had, with YARD, produced dramatically more efficient steam propulsion (from oil fuel or nuclear power). There were two great new diesel developments, there was hydrogen peroxide for submarines and lastly, as time passed, there was the ultimate winner, gas turbines. The 'weapon revolution', triggered by the newly formed seagoing and intellectually well qualified (L) electrical branch and ordnance specialisation (O/E) (today merged as the (W/E) weapon engineering sub-specialisation), was starting to provide the Navy with the weapons it had lacked, and the (A/E) (air engineering sub-specialisation) some of whom also became outstanding test pilots, was working towards its present highly manpower economic serviceability rate for fixed and rotary wing aircraft at sea and ashore, said by some to outmatch anything the US Services or the RAF can achieve.

Chapter 9
The Special Relationship

Neither the sure prevention of war nor the continuous rise of world organisation will be gained without what I have called the fraternal association of English speaking peoples. This means a special relationship between the British Commonwealth and Empire and the United States. This is no time for generalities. I venture to be precise. Fraternal association requires not only the growing friendship and mutual understanding between our two vast but kindred systems of society, but the continuance of the intimate relations between our military advisers, leading to a common study of potential dangers, similarity of weapons and manuals of instruction and interchange of officers and cadets at colleges. It should carry with it the continuance of the present facilities for mutual security by the joint use of all naval and air force bases in the possession of either country all over the world.

Winston Churchill,
speech of 5th March 1946 at Fulton, Missouri

As I have recorded in *The Man Around the Engine,* I first became aware of the reality of the special relationship between the USN and the RN as the sun set on September 2nd 1945 over Tokyo Bay and Fujiyama's snow capped peak glowed red. After a forenoon of rejoicing and thankfulness which had seen the surrender of Japan aboard the great USS *Missouri,* a moment which had rightly belonged to the United States as the ending to the greatest and bloodiest maritime campaign the world has known, the Royal Navy could again resume one aspect of a peacetime routine. On September 2nd 1939 the ceremony of 'sunset' had been enacted throughout the British fleets worldwide and at 'colours' on September 3rd the ensigns were hoisted once more. Now six bloody years later to the very day, those White Ensigns, flown by day and night ever since, could be lowered. As the last notes of the evening hymn died away, interspersed with the sunset call as only Royal Marine buglers can sound it, and the ensigns came down, it could be seen that in all the US ships men were standing at attention, facing the British flagship and saluting. The Royal and Merchant Navies alone, they were acknowledging, had fought from the beginning to the very end.

I was aware that such a relationship still existed when, on leaving Washington after three years as naval attaché, I received a model of a joining shackle of an anchor cable, together with a message from the Chief of the Bureau of Ships, Admiral Galantin, with whom, as an engineer, I had a very close professional relationship. He wrote, 'I hope as you leave our shores you will accept this model as a token of the way our two navies must always remain joined together to keep open the ocean highways whatever storms we may have to face'. That the relationship still exists twenty years later was demonstrated just seven days into the Iraqi crisis, when President Bush (ex Lieutenant USNR) wrote, 'Dear Louis, *The Man Around the Engine* arrived today and will accompany me to Kennebunkport tomorrow...Warmest personal regards and so many thanks'.

Some would ascribe this special relationship to common ancestry. Others would suggest the importance of a common language but, though there may be something in that, derivations of English are now common throughout the international community. In the naval context, many would ascribe great importance to the British Navy Staff, concentrated in Washington DC. Others would say that the sense of tradition of the older Navy appeals to the USN, just as the writings of Admiral Mahan USN are absorbed by many wise British Naval officers. Whatever the origin of the relationship, it is certain that the constant interchange of weapon development and tactical expertise, so fruitful for both navies, cements the relationship and makes it rather more special than that existing between the other two fighting services.

Some suggest that the intelligence exchange is the prime factor in the special relationship between the two nations; and like the naval relationship there is probably something in that. Nevertheless while the personal contacts between the State department in Foggy Bottom and the Foreign and Commonwealth office are close and, thanks to the British Embassy in Washington DC, most certainly genial, the results are sometimes less happy than should be the case.

History seems to suggest that the ancestry of the extraordinary naval entente stretches back to the friendship between the then Captains (later Admirals) Jellicoe (RN) and Sims (USN) before and during World War I. If these two were the progenitors then it was Churchill, in his speech at Fulton, who really gave substance to the concept. Churchill clearly placed the task of maintaining this relationship upon the shoulders of the services and few would doubt, given his acquaintanceship with Jellicoe and Sims and the correspondence between himself as 'a former naval person' and Franklin Roosevelt, former assistant secretary to the USN, that he looked to the Royal Navy to play a significant part in sustaining it. It has, and it still does.

Ambassador David Bruce, in an address to The Pilgrims, the society dedicated to enhancing the special relationship once said, 'The essential factor in any alliance is trust. Given the strength and imperatives of national self interest, such trust can never be complete, but that between our two countries is fuller than can be found in the rest of the world.'

Lord Balfour too hit the nail on the head when he remarked, 'The United States and England are so fundamentally at one that they can safely afford to bicker, so sure of their own moderation that they are not dangerously disturbed by the never ending din of political conflict.'

The never ending din of political conflict is something from which the services are slightly, but never wholly, insulated. The UK is still, despite the Channel Tunnel (so vulnerable to terrorists from within and on the sea bed) and hopes of being politically at the heart of the Community, an island state on the ocean flank of Europe facing the Atlantic and the United States. Twice this century the South-West approaches have been the graveyard of the merchant navy, whose losses brought us to the verge of starvation and surrender. Even France, Spain, The Netherlands, Norway, and Portugal no longer look so much to the oceans as once they did.

Despite glasnost and perestroika the Soviet Union is still reported as sending a nuclear hunter-killer submarine down the slips every six weeks and has transferred many thousands of men from her army to her navy. In this noisy age it is difficult, especially for politicians, not to sacrifice the hopes of the future for the clamorous demands of the present. It must continually be drummed into younger statesmen that the future is not foreseeable and that an older generation still recalls that twice this century the Atlantic Bridge, over which must flow reinforcements in war and raw materials in peace, has almost been brought down, and with it the country, to destruction. Britain rightly still provides about 60% of the Eastern Atlantic maritime defence at a cost of only 23% of the defence budget. Even if a concerted EC defence policy was slowly to emerge, this role, which depends on the special relationship, will surely continue as a major part of Britain's contribution to the community.

As Third Sea Lord and Controller in 1939 Admiral Bruce Fraser (later Admiral of the Fleet Lord Fraser) saw for himself how ill-equipped the Navy was for war compared to its US counterpart. Later as Commander in Chief, in succession, of three great fleets, the Home Fleet, the East Indies Fleet and, in particular, the British Pacific Fleet, his experiences showed him that the Royal Navy lacked mobility and was backward in its weapon fits compared to the US Navy.

Warships take a decade to design and build. They are expensive and becoming more so, but they last a long time. Weapons have moved in half a century from the gun to the anti-missile missile, and this last development has made surface and sub-surface warships less vulnerable to air attack, but no navy can be built and armed and trained in a sudden emergency. This Fraser well understood when he reached the top.

Fraser's task on becoming First Sea Lord in 1948 was no easy one. The UK was virtually bankrupt. The Chiefs of Staff, thanks to Montgomery and Tedder and the Secretary of State, Mr A V Alexander, were at each other's throats. NATO was still just a piece of paper. The Berlin blockade was at its height, and war with the Soviets

Admiral of the Fleet Lord Fraser of North Cape (photograph courtesy IWM).

seemed imminent. The Army in Europe and Palestine necessarily took up half the defence vote, the RAF more than a quarter and the Navy had to make do with whatever was left. Ten battleships, twenty cruisers, thirty seven Escort carriers, sixty destroyers and eighty Flower class corvettes, most of which in 1939–40 Fraser had himself conceived, had already been sent to the scrapheap. A defence statement in March 1948 had insisted that 'it was necessary for the Navy to bring down its manpower as rapidly as possible and accept a degree of disorganisation and immobility'. Though Fraser's anger could incinerate, as he had shown when HMS *Euryalus* had booed his flagship in Hong-Kong, he was the kindest and most human of men and he well knew what 'disorganisation' would entail for the ordinary sailor.

There was one bright spot. Field Marshal Slim, a man who, like Fraser, watched over those who served him, no matter how lowly, and who had also experienced those two impostors triumph and disaster, soon relieved Montgomery. The Chiefs of Staff meetings were once more fairly amicable.

As far as the Navy was concerned Fraser saw with a blinding clarity what had to be done. The Navy had to have its mobility restored. The relationship with the USN had to be sustained and brought even closer. The Navy had to make much more use of advancing technology and apply it to the lessons learnt in war, especially in the fields of air and submarine warfare. There had to be some sort of reversion to the Lord Fisher concept for the officer corps, of 'some community of knowledge and a lifelong community of sentiment'.

Where mobility was concerned, Fraser, when Commander in Chief British Pacific Fleet, had already been told that war experienced junior officers in the department of the Engineer in Chief, with the active help of the Chief of Bureau of Ships in Washington DC, were striving to improve mobility. To give them more ammunition he ordered me, then acting chief engineer of his flagship, to consult with my opposite numbers in the fleet and co-ordinate a 'worm's eye' view, as those down below saw it, as to why the British Fleet lacked the amazing mobility that had enabled the US navy to conduct their historic maritime campaign throughout the vast wastes of the Pacific ocean. By then Fraser's experience of the operational capability of USN ships under his command in the Home Fleet, and his period of visiting the US Pacific Fleet (when he was nearly killed by a Kamikaze) had convinced him that there was much to be learned from the US Navy not only in the actual designing of ships and machinery, but also in terms of officer training, particularly in the realms of technology.

Fraser was a man of great humility and patience, as he had shown when turning down Churchill's offer of the post of First Sea Lord after Sir Dudley Pound died in harness, and he knew that 'Rome was not built in a day'. However, the committees and working parties he established as First Sea Lord, and the encouragement he gave to those inaugurated by his predecessor, coupled with the battle experienced officers he brought to his Board and onto the naval staff, as well as to the department of the Engineer in Chief, provided a concerted drive towards the shaping of a new fleet, men and materiel, based on new technology applied to lessons learnt and the future of maritime war as far as it could be foreseen.

By the time Fraser left the Admiralty in 1951 (sadly estranged from Winston Churchill who deprecated Fraser's pro-USN view that the Supreme Allied Commander, Atlantic must inevitably be an American operating from Norfolk, Virginia), the naval staff were demanding a frigate that could cross the Atlantic without refuelling, and all existing ships and those on the design board were at last being fitted to refuel at sea as Lord Fisher had proposed forty years before. The design departments were under scrutiny from a war-wise Controller, while the results of the Noble committee and the Brind and Montague working parties (all concerned with different aspects of personnel policy) were leading up to the Mansergh committee which would reshape the whole officer structure to make it more relevant to a smaller ship smaller Navy and, by investing naval engineers with more influence, more responsive to the hectic onrush of technology.

On Fraser's 81st birthday, I was fortunate to be the only other guest when Admiral Sir Michael Le Fanu, then First Sea Lord (who had been liaison officer with the US Pacific Fleet and Lord Fraser's naval assistant), gave Lord Fraser a celebratory lunch. I was naval attaché in the States at the time, and these two great men left me with two abiding pieces of their wisdom. Everything possible should be done to ensure the continuation of the relationship between the two navies, and (to me as an engineer most interestingly) it could be that where the RN in the past had abandoned Fisher's ideas and had been remiss in giving its seamen officers insufficient technological training, it should never go too far in the opposite direction and fall into the trap, as the USN had tended to do, of 'enervating the command' by overtraining deck officers technically at the expense of their 'sea-sense' and their understanding of tactics and weapon usage.

A man untrained in any knowledge of modern technology suffers a serious impoverishment in his intellectual life. That had been the trouble with many RN deck officers who suffered from the anti-engineering influences at Dartmouth since the Board of Admiralty abrogated most of Fisher's ideas in 1925. The professional technologist, civilian or service, must also possess special personal qualities of leadership and must know how to handle men, and this quality can only be gained by personal contact and never through books. A naval engineer, besides acquiring those qualities of leadership needed in action below the waterline, in an operations room or in the air, must also be able to interpret scientific advance to a technically literate (but not necessarily technologically professionally trained) naval staff responsible for meeting the threat. Besides this the naval engineer must be able also to lead civilian designers towards the needs of a warship operating in an environment likely to alienate any normal land based mechanism, to which the civilian designer is generally more accustomed.

A middle course must be steered which will give the RN the best of both worlds, captains of war and professional engineers. With the increasingly sophisticated maritime weapons, no one sort of man can absorb it all. Deck officers, technically fully literate, provide one element; professional technologists with a practical knowledge derived from service at sea or in the air, another; and technicians who can watch over the machinery and weapons and keep them serviceable, a third.

What Lord Fraser had in fact told me was brought home to me a few weeks later when I was staying with a US Admiral responsible for all the training of the 6th fleet in the Pacific. He was deeply concerned because there had been a terrible collision in which the officer of the watch, who had won every academic prize that he could during his years of training, had failed dismally at a moment of crisis and lives had been lost. A long discussion well into the night, lubricated with much Jack Daniels (always a great aid to the special relationship) led us to the conclusion that whereas the RN's general lack of maritime technology in 1939 and lack of mobility in the Pacific might well have been in great part due to the lack of any technological education of RN deck officers responsible for conceiving the warship (staff) requirements, this particular collision probably occurred because an exceptionally academically able young USN officer lacked that almost unidentifiable quality, a 'sea sense' which, except in rare cases, comes only from experience and probably many close shaves.

To turn away from Lord Fraser and the essential need for a special relationship between the RN and the USN in war and in the preparation for war, there is also a role for this relationship in peacetime operations. When the fifth Polaris submarine was cancelled in the late 1960s the managing director of Vickers (the builders), calling on me in Washington DC, asked me what I thought he should do with the skilled surplus design capacity at Barrow. At the time an officer on my staff, Surgeon-Commander later Vice Admiral Sir John Rawlins, engaged in one of the many naval elements of the special relationship, was helping to teach the United States Navy to live on the floor of the ocean and, thanks to the USN, I was fairly well aware of the resources lying on the sea bed. I told the Vickers MD that this was where the future lay. Later, with the help of Lord Mountbatten and Lord Zuckerman, the exploration of the sea bed as an aspect of our national defence policy was taken up with the then Prime Minister, Mr Harold Wilson.

The Navy has to be kept busy in peacetime. Without continuing (though not necessarily continuous) sea time any navy is apt to lose its touch. There is normally plenty for the RN and the USN to do, but in the short spells of peace which occasionally interrupt the normal flow of world conflict the two navies should continue to cooperate. Outer space has gripped the public imagination as the unexplored wealth of the abyssal depths and the ocean floor have, as yet, failed to do. Besides the policing of the oceans and ensuring its own readiness for war, only the Navy is available to expand UK knowledge of the sea's resources and the wealth of the sea bed. Without knowing the detailed reasons, the abandoning of HMS *Challenger*, the most sophisticated sea bed exploration ship in the world seemed to me to be a catastrophe.

If peace prevails, the sea bed will be part of the answer to the 200 per minute increase in the world's population and the present breakneck squandering of the land's mineral resources. Wealth anywhere is apt to provoke conflict. Peace will not bring a diminution but an increase in the maritime responsibilities, including that special relationship with the USN that our great predecessors have handed on to us, if the wealth that lies in the ocean depths is to be harnessed and peacefully harvested.

In the words of the Charter of the Institution of Civil Engineers an engineer's job is 'to direct the great services of power in nature for the use and convenience of man'. Ocean engineering is inevitably touched on at the Royal Naval Engineering College. There are good grounds for establishing a full syllabus as part of a small naval engineering specialisation akin to the present marine, air and weapon specialisations, to build on the great undersea experience that now exists in the civilian sector, most of it originally gleaned from the Navy.

History may show that it was Lord Fraser, as First Sea Lord, and Admiral Sir Michael Denny as Controller and then Head of the British Joint Services Mission in Washington DC, and Admirals Sir Peter Reid and Le Fanu as Controllers, who showed the Royal Navy, in the context of the Cold War and the Soviet threat, how to use new technology and at the same time strive to reinforce the special relationship with the USN. The Soviet threat may or may not have been extinguished, but even if it has only diminished the world faces the more imminent threat of over population. The two most sophisticated navies, one small and one very large, may have, in their special relationship and their understanding of the oceans, a great deal of the expertise to meet the critical resource problems of the next few decades from which, human nature being what it is, conflict will surely arise.

Chapter 10
The Navy's Oil

The Royal Commission on Fuel and Engines 1912
—The Geddes Committee 1950

To commit the navy irrevocably to oil was indeed 'to take arms against a sea of troubles'...Yet beyond the breakers was a great hope...better ships, better crews, higher economies, more intense forms of warpower—in a word, mastery itself was the prize of the venture...Forward then.

The World Crisis, Vol 1
Winston Churchill

It is not too far fetched to assert that, having been shown by Fisher and his Royal Commission how oil could inevitably lead the Royal Navy along the path to more intense forms of warpower the Admiralty, as so often in the past, just as inevitably lost the way.

The failure to make full tactical use of the oil fired Queen Elizabeths at Jutland was the first truly operational mistake in a more generally depressing catalogue stretching over thirty years. The overall neglect of the benefits of oil fuel was due, in part, to the Treasury who, as they have so often done, permitted economic to outweigh military considerations. For the financial pundits there was even less excuse than usual. Prior to 1914 the Admiralty had invested over £2M in the Anglo-Persian Oil Co which bought a seat on the Board of that company for the Secretary of the Admiralty. By the end of World War I, even though naval fuel oil had been purchased at well below market rates, the dividends accruing to the naval vote had paid for the whole of the 1912–1914 building programme. The failure to comprehend the war fighting merits of oil fuel was notably carried forward in the post war years by a naval staff obsessed by fear of technological progress and a particular aversion to those who sought it. Few, if any, of the elements of increased warpower made possible by the use of oil were ever incorporated in the Staff requirements, which laid down the aims for which designers should strive when building a post (World War I) Navy.

Thus it was that when Mussolini entered the war in 1940 and the Mediterranean was closed to tanker passage, the Home Fleet in Scapa Flow had to turn to fuels from the Western Hemisphere. Unknown to the Royal Navy the constituents of such fuels, particularly in their asphalt, vanadium and sulphur content and their lack of wax, were wholly different to the premium fuels purchased from Persia during the long years of peace. The Royal Commission had mentioned the dangers of tying the Fleet to one fuel, but this had been forgotten or overtaken by the economic attraction of the cheaper fuel. It had also recommended heating for above ground storages and pipelines so that fuels less pumpable in cold weather could, if necessary, be used. This essential measure too was put on one side on the grounds of economy. So the Fleet's burning equipment in 1939 was insufficiently flexible to cope with Western fuels, and smoke, a hazard in pre-radar days permitting enemy ships an early sighting, not to speak of hostile submarines, was an ever present danger almost impossible to prevent. Besides smoke caused by poor combustion, the sulphur and vanadium constituents in Western fuels gave rise to corrosion problems and to collapses in the furnace brickwork.

There was another almost inexplicable failure by the post-war Boards of Admiralty. One of the major reasons put forward by the Royal Commission for turning from coal to oil was that thereby the Fleet would be able to fuel when underway at sea and thus immediately be reinforced by the 25% of ships normally coaling in harbour. The mobility acquired by a fleet able to fuel at sea was never recognised. Until 1945 the time honoured method of refuelling was for a smaller tanker to carry fuel from large tankers or shore storage and pump it over when either alongside or sometimes from astern of the warship, in harbour or at anchor. The advances in lubricating oil techniques had also been wholly neglected in the Royal Navy. Sperm oil (from whales) was still in use, and one of the party tricks of a chief artificer in HMS *Forres*, the small coal fired sloop in which Dartmouth cadets sicked their way round the South Coast, was to take a mouthful of sperm oil and spit it onto the moving parts of *Forres'* reciprocating engines. Special mineral lubricating oil, with properties that prevented it emulsifying when it mixed with steam from turbine glands came uniquely from one well in Pennsylvania, as it had when Sir Charles Parsons demonstrated the *Turbinia* years before.

The 'worm's eye' view report (*chapter 9*) recorded many of these deficiencies and how the USN was equipped to fuel rapidly at sea from specially fitted tankers and how it used an additive turbine lubricating oil with superior properties, and much greater ease of supply to that of special mineral lubricating oil. In summing up the operating differences between the two navies the report suggested that good overall design, close attention to many of the Royal Commission recommendations, and a better attitude to and understanding of engineering amongst all USN officers, were the main reasons which gave the USN a mobility so infinitely superior to that of the RN. The astonishing (by British standards, but compared to the USN very modest) availability of the British Pacific Fleet was due to the superior quality and training (particularly) of long service RN personnel and a resolute refusal to conform to many of the edicts emanating from the Admiralty or laid down in the British Naval Engineering Manual.

In the immediate aftermath of World War II all this was recognised by Rear-Admiral (E) D C Ford, then deputy engineer in chief in charge at Bath, because he had been Fleet Engineer officer in Scapa as had his eventual successor Rear-Admiral (E) The Hon Denis Maxwell. Both were imbued with the need to improve the mobility of the Navy, and both (and Rear-Admiral (E) C H Nicholson in charge of appointing) saw the need to inject wholly new thinking into the engineering design department. They arranged for senior officers from a wide variety of engineering experience, marine, air, ordnance and dockyards to be appointed to key posts.

It was recognised that the Engineer in Chief was de facto and de jure responsible for the quality of all forms of petroleum products in use in the Navy. In the locust years, the directors of contracts and stores had continued to purchase such fuels and lubricants as seemed appropriate without any well informed guidance, other than that of precedent or price. Happily, thanks to the experience of the stores department, the quality of purchases had been retained, although very little advance had been made into the rapidly developing petroleum products brought about by the war.

In seeking to assume his responsibilities for quality the Engineer in Chief ran into a major problem. There was no-one in his depart-

ment who had anything but a rudimentary knowledge of the petroleum world. The only source of advice on which he could lay his
hands was a 'dagger' Lieutenant-Commander (E), shortly Commander (E), Edward Tyrrell. The latter's unique ability rested solely
on what he had learnt about petroleum technology from Dutch fellow prisoners of war even though in captivity, being exceptionally
brave and aggressive by nature, Tyrrell had suffered more inhuman
treatment than most from his Japanese captors. So Tyrrell, with the
help of one leading draughtsman, Mr Ninnim, was appointed to the
design department to establish a fuels and lubricants section and
prepare to correct the negligence of three decades.

A year or so later I was rescued from limbo by Admiral Ford who
had taken a much less hostile attitude to my worms eye view report
than those in the engineering hierarchy who had originally read it.
Ford arranged for me to spend a year at the University of Birmingham studying petroleum technology under Professor F H Garner
OBE, the Dean of the Faculty of Science and a noted petroleum ex-
pert. Here I found myself one of a mob of (mostly) ex RAF officers
studying for their degrees on Forces Educational Grants; young men
with old faces from bomber command, whose record of courage has
never been properly acknowledged but who, amongst the many
kindnesses they showed me, gave me an abiding respect and admiration for their service. I managed to arrange for some of the younger
students, whose call-up had been postponed, to do their national
service in the Navy.

It was at Birmingham that I first began to understand the international implications of petroleum supply. Amongst the students were
a number of young Iranians sent there by the Anglo-Iranian Oil
Company (ex Anglo-Persian) for training before taking over the
management of the great refinery at Abadan. Their extensive allowances made them a target of jealousy for the very much less finan-
cially solvent Britons. For the Navy they had a particular distaste.
The cheap oil enjoyed by the RN had restricted dividends and profit
accruing to Iran, but the complaint could have been easily settled
had it not been for the regime of Mossadeq and the whimsical attitude of the Iranian Majlis which, together, were holding up negotia-
tions. In the end we made friends and I often wonder if any of them
now run their great petroleum industry.

My period at Birmingham coincided with a serious, and at first
unrecognised, oil problem directly affecting the mobility of the fleet.

This concerned the pumpability of naval fuels and the problem had political, financial, technical and climatic implications.

Simplistically, the merchant navy and industry normally used a very viscous (sticky) fuel then known as bunker C, which they could store in conveniently adjacent tanks from which it could flow by gravity or, if heated, be pumped to the fuel burning equipment under boilers. RN ships could not use such a fuel for three good reasons. First, one of the great advantages of oil over coal was the flexibility it gave to the speed variations needed in war. Sudden speed changes required sudden changes in the rate fuel flowed to the burners (sprayers) which could never be varied quickly with a thick viscous fuel. Second, a highly viscous fuel, while possible to stow in large tanks adjacent to the boilers in merchantmen, would mean putting 'all eggs in one basket' in a warship and then one hit could remove the fuel supply. In warships the fuel is necessarily stowed all over the ship in small compartments which are part of damage limitation design, and from these it must be readily pumpable. Last, as the RN had so belatedly learned from the USN in the Pacific, real mobility derived from being able to refuel quickly when underway; and this again required a very easily pumpable fuel.

Bunker C clearly met none of these requirements, but the strongest political and financial pressures were being exerted by technically illiterate politicians and civil servants to change to bunker C and to forego the lighter middle distillate diluent needed by the Navy's pumpability requirement.

As already mentioned (*chapters 6 and 7*) the closing of the Mediterranean route for tankers and the long run round the Cape of Good Hope had meant that much of the Navy had had to change to fuel from the Western Hemisphere and the constituents of such fuels were very different to those from the Persian Gulf. To ensure that the Western fuels were of a suitable and consistent standard an ad hoc specification had been agreed during the war, applicable particularly to these fuels. One of the differences in fuel behaviour between the Western and Gulf fuels was that while both became more viscous in cold temperatures the Western fuels remained pumpable longer than the Gulf fuels which were apt to 'gel' (solidify) rather suddenly and remain unpumpable until the temperature rose considerably. It was for this reason that the Royal Commission in 1913 had specified the inclusion in the Persian fuel of a considerable quantity of middle distillate which permitted a much lower ambient temperature before 'gelling' occurred. At the same time the Commission had recommended that heating should be fitted both in ships (as was done) and in above ground installations (which was not), in case, in the future, fuels more apt to become unpumpable in cold weather became the sole source of supply.

When the war ended Persian fuels again became available at a marked down price and were routinely purchased, and above and underground storages filled, but the purchase was not to the original Royal Commission fuel specification as had been the practice pre-war. Instead the ad hoc specification, used principally during the war for the supply of Western fuels, was used.

The winter of 1946/1947 was one of the worst this century and, for a bankrupt but victorious Britain, lease lend withdrawn without warning, worse in many ways than the war years, albeit without the bombing. Apart from the cold and the lack of coal for heating, for gas supplies or electricity generation, even bread was rationed, which had never happened during the struggle. Practically the only UK negotiable asset was that fraction of Persian middle distillate which could be purchased at a knock down sterling price and sold (for dollars) for heating oil to keep America warm in an even worse winter.

A distraught ministry of fuel and power, the Treasury, the oil companies, and a totally ignorant Admiralty, when applying the current wartime ad hoc specification (created for the supply of Western fuels) to the Persian production found to their delight that little or no diluent was needed to meet the specified viscosity at *normal* operating temperatures. The pressures to change to bunker C eased and Persian fuel was purchased at an even cheaper than anticipated price because, in the case of the ad hoc specification naval fuel, it needed much less middle distillate, which could instead be turned into heating oil and sold for precious dollars.

It was not till the Spring of 1947 that the Director of Stores discovered that in many above ground tanks the fuel so recently procured had 'gelled' to the extent that when a 56lb weight was dropped through a manhole, it bounced! There was much scratching of heads and at first the phenomenon was ascribed to incompatibility between the fuel residues of Western fuels already in the tanks and the newly purchased Persian fuel. Gradually the awful truth dawned. The exceptionally low temperatures had caused the Persian fuel in above ground tanks to 'gel', though mercifully this had not happened in the underground storages, where the constant temperature was marginally above the gelling point. This disaster was due to a lack of middle distillate and a lack of tank and fuel line heating as originally recommended by the Royal Commission.

By now it was 1948. Russia was on the rampage. Berlin was blockaded. The Western Union Alliance had come into being. The devastated countries of Western Europe once more looked to the UK for a lead as the Iron Curtain came down from Stettin to Trieste, and as 'stay behind' parties were recruited against an expected invasion by the Red Army. It was in these circumstances that the three Admiralty departments responsible for the quality, purchase and storage of fuel had to write a joint Minute to the Board. The gist was, 'should the Soviet blockade of Berlin escalate into war and should the forthcoming winter be once again of great severity, then the Board should be aware that there is enough boiler fuel in underground storages (where the temperature remains sufficiently high to keep the fuel pumpable) to activate the Reserve Fleet and refuel a fully mobilised fleet after one sortie. Thereafter further active operations may have to await the advent of warmer weather.'

By this time Commander Tyrrell had laid the groundwork for a completely new look on petroleum affairs in the Navy. With the development of the Admiralty standard range and high speed Deltic diesel engines *(chapter 8)* he had alerted the designers to the improved engine performances offered by the newly developing additive detergent lubricants. Sperm oil was on the way out, as was special mineral lubricating oil, to be replaced with new additive oils. Tyrrell had also begun to educate a reluctant weapon department into some understanding of what was becoming possible in the new world of petroleum technology. It is hard to overstate his contribution to the future improvement of Royal Naval mobility and weapon design.

The rising and apparently imminent Soviet threat to Western Europe suddenly imposed a difficult task on all the services and, in the case of the Engineer in Chief's department, especially on the new fuels and lubricants specialist section. When Ernest Bevin signed the Brussels Treaty and the Western Union was born, standardisation of petroleum products between the different armies, air forces and navies of the Benelux alliance became essential; and they all looked to Britain (Tyrrell) for a lead. These increasing international obligations took up so much of his time in travelling (in those days by train and boat) to Paris, Brussels and The Hague that, in trying to overcome the

British naval fuel problems, Tyrrell had found it difficult to 'hold the line'. So little seemed to be known about the behaviour of fuel oils, even by the great oil companies, and so overwhelming was the pressure to economise on middle distillate in the search for dollars, that a way forward was difficult for him or anyone else immediately to discern.

Here Professor Garner saved the Navy's bacon. Like Garner, Tyrrell was anxious to educate me before I relieved him and he kept me in touch, particularly with the fuel problem and this, in turn, I inflicted on Garner. The latter was quick to comprehend the Royal Navy's needs and the difficulties. With his wide experience and his knowledge of the Petroleum Industry he perceived all sides of the problem and realised, probably more than any of us, that there was no facile solution which would satisfy the Navy, the industry, the Treasury and the ministry of fuel and power. The international need for a fuel usable by the Western Union (and later NATO, by then in the final stage of gestation) did not make the problem any easier. Garner took me to meetings with the companies and the ministry of fuel and power and it was clear that, with the exception of the Anglo-Iranian Oil Co, they could see no reason why the Royal Navy needed a different fuel to the Merchant Navy; while the RN, with its hitherto total ignorance of petroleum affairs had never thought to explain (and indeed had been unable to explain) its needs, in words the companies could understand.

After six weeks experience of the load Tyrrell had so successfully carried I collapsed with acute jaundice. On my return the assistant engineer in chief to whom I reported instructed me to set aside all international and lubricant problems, and write him a paper with an accurate history of Royal Naval fuel affairs since Churchill had approved the change from coal to oil in 1913. It was a measure of the Navy's neglect that after Churchill's minute and signature forty years before there were no more entries in the docket so the preparation of a summary did not take long once research had revealed the relevant file. Within a few months a formal memorandum from the Engineer in Chief of the Fleet to the Board of Admiralty was prepared and the actions proposed therein quickly approved. Four steps were considered necessary.

1. A revision of Board instructions more precisely defining departmental responsibility for petroleum products.

2. The adequate staffing and equipping of an Admiralty laboratory as a physical, chemical and engine testing station for petroleum products of use to the Navy.

3. The establishment of an Admiralty/oil industry committee to revise the 1913 specification in the light of present knowledge and conditions; and to advise on other present and future naval fuel and lubricant problems.

4. The formulation of practical measures designed to reduce the Navy's requirement for middle distillate.

The Admiralty side of the committee, in accordance with step 3, consisted of the deputy directors of stores and contracts and the deputy Engineer in Chief. There was also a representative from the ministry of fuel and power and an observer from the US navy, as NATO had just emerged and inter-operability had to be assured. Admiral Mountbatten, by now Fourth Sea Lord and responsible, inter alia, for this part of the Navy's affairs, typically entered the fray and wrote personally to the chairmen of the companies concerned asking for cooperation and for the attendance of a senior executive (the names having been supplied by Garner) who would be able to commit his company if and when the committee reached a consensus on a solution to the problems confronting them. Garner also brought onto the committee a number of independent experts who could never be accused of commercial bias, a factor about which the deputy director of contracts was quite properly, but as it turned out quite needlessly, somewhat concerned. I was nominated co-secretary with Mr Pat Lovett, an able naval stores officer (and later Director of Stores).

The appointment of a chairman produced a problem. Garner put forward The Hon Ross Geddes (later Lord Geddes), the son of a British ambassador to Washington and therefore au fait with the US scene. Geddes had acquired a mechanical science tripos from Cambridge, he had served as a marine engineer in Cunard/White Star and, because of poor eyesight had served in the tanker division of the ministry of fuel and power during the war, with great success. There were other nominees, and the Secretary of the Admiralty recoiled at the name, as Ross Geddes' uncle, Eric Geddes, had been responsible for the infamous 'Geddes axe' after World War I. The Secretary was not aware, however, that Ross Geddes' sister was married to Prince Louis of Hesse, Lord Mountbatten's cousin and the Fourth Sea Lord knew Geddes well, so an exceptionally able chairman was made available to help the Admiralty and the oil companies to find a satisfactory modus vivendi for the future.

There were two sub-committees. The first was to examine the technical details of the Navy's fuel problems with Professor Garner as chairman and the second, under the chairmanship of Dr (later Sir Charles) Cawley, was to deal with lubricant problems. These two sub-committees reported every two months to a meeting of the main committee.

Simultaneously, first the Western Union and then NATO became concerned, and it fell to me to chair the Northern (Norway and Denmark and UK), Central (France, Belgium, The Netherlands, Canada, USA and UK) and Southern (Italy and UK) fuels and lubricants nomenclature and standardisation committees besides the UK inter-Service equivalents. NATO security regulations at first required this curious division so that with the invaluable help of the tri-lingual secretary and interpreter, Lieutenant-Commander Alec Lacy, I found myself the link between each of the Regions and the UK. Amazingly much of the common nomenclature we invented still seems to prevail.

Geddes was a first class chairman and with a complete absence of friction the oil companies came to understand and help with the Na-

Mr M Montgomery, Sir Charles Cawley, secretary, Lord Geddes and the author (l–r), members of the Geddes committee of 1950, aboard RMS Queen Elizabeth (photograph author's collection).

vy's needs; and the Navy advanced hesitantly into the new world of petroleum. By May 1951 an interim fuel specification for the Royal Navy, acceptable both to the allies and the USN, was in place and agreed with the ministry of fuel and power and the companies. The Admiralty was recommended to establish a purely Naval investigational and quality surveillance organisation with centralised and adequate laboratory facilities.

Besides the many great men of the petroleum industry (particularly Sir Maurice Banks of AIOC and Mr Frank Jones of British-Mexican Oil Co) who, at a time of great pressure for most of them, gave their time unstintingly to solving the Navy's problems, the service owes a great debt to the Institute of Petroleum. At the first post war Petroleum Congress at The Hague, attended by more than a thousand petroleum technologists from all over the world, the President invited me to chair some of the meetings, thus not only enhancing the Royal Navy's status as a major client, but also providing the opportunity to discuss existing and possible future fuel and lubricant developments relevant to all navies in the Western Alliance with that most powerful body of oil technologists.

Towards the end of the committee's work a quorum travelled by train to Genoa to board HMS *Vanguard* and observe the onboard management of fuel oil known as 'ballasting'. This system, specially designed by the Director of Naval Construction, required oil fuel to be displaced by sea-water, from a tank low down in the ship into ready use tanks. Its purpose was to increase the stability of the ship by keeping the tank full (of oil or sea-water) thus lowering the centre of gravity (and increasing stability) by off-setting to some extent the top weight then becoming inevitable due to heavy radar aerials high up on the masts.

Unfortunately, in this case, the Chief Stoker operating the system, observing the increasingly green complexions of the quorum as they peered into an oil filling funnel into which displaced fuel should soon arrive, panicked. He opened the sea inlet too fast, the sea water channelled up through the fuel it was meant to displace slowly, and a water/fuel emulsion emerged into the filling funnel leading to the ready-use tank.

The committee's worst fears were realised and as the Chairman wrote to the Fourth Sea Lord on our return, 'None of us have ever seen so much care and ingenuity devoted to designing a system to transfer oil from one unsuitable receptacle to another; and at the same time injecting into it saltwater, far beyond the limits permitted by specification. Such limits are only met with great difficulty by the suppliers and at great expense to the Navy.'

The Director of Naval Construction was not amused.

Whether by accident or design I have never discovered, but this was my swansong; and I was dispatched as chief engineer and Fleet Engineer Officer, South Atlantic to HMS *Bermuda*, flagship of the South Atlantic Squadron, somewhat scurrilously known at that time as 'The Legion of the Damned'. There, besides working with the brave South African Navy whose exploits around Tobruk I well remembered and as I have recounted in *The Man Around the Engine*, I indulged in what Defence Statements refer to as 'showing the flag'. Such activity, in this case stretching over several thousand miles meant visiting Lourenco Marques (as was), Durban, East London, Port Elizabeth, Capetown, Saldanha Bay, Luanda, Fernando Po, Lagos, Takoradi, Freetown, Bathurst, Dakar, St Helena, Ascension and Tristan da Cunha, and entertaining, largely at our own expense, the cheerful, sometimes inebriated, but always interesting and welcoming inhabitants of all those ports and islands, while our families led a rather lonely and penurious existence in Simonstown.

Part 3   The General List of Officers

Chapter 11
Future Officer Structure

The Mansergh Committee 1954–1955

> *In considering the general body of officers...one is on surer ground.*
> *Here is a power of unyielding endurance...and a capacity for*
> *initiative which cannot be checked except by supine leadership. The*
> *impress of naval discipline is constant. With this there goes the gifted*
> *and light-hearted understatement which is paralleled in no Navy in*
> *the world.*
>
>

The Naval Heritage
Archbishop David Mathew

The restoration of mobility after 1945 and the powerful oceanic reach
of maritime power, was seen by wise senior officers, as Fisher had
understood, to be not simply the product of sophisticated
engineering *design*. Total warship design, they realised, must be the
product of an officer corps, all of them technologically minded, but
including a proportion of naval engineering professionals with sea
sense. This mix should be more able to guide non-seagoing civilian
designers, in the many relevant engineering disciplines, towards the
practical application of scientific and engineering advance
applicable to maritime warfare on, over and under the oceans.

In the first twenty five years of the twentieth century the Navy's
officer structure had been subjected to two complete upheavals. In
addition the Geddes axe in the aftermath of World War I had evicted,
with minimal compensation, many of those officers, some of them
potentially brilliant, mistakenly brought in on a permanent career
basis to man up the vast wartime fleets.

The first upheaval had been the result of the Selborne–Fisher
reforms. Rather than a wholly separate entry and training for naval
engineers these reforms envisaged a single cadet entry from which

would evolve specialist gunnery (G), navigation (N), torpedoes (T) or marine engineering (E), Naval officers and Royal Marines, whose roles would it was hoped, be interchangeable after the equivalent rank of commander. As was explained in earlier chapters the idea of interchangeability was never set in concrete; and quite soon the idea of Royal Marine and Naval officers undergoing identical training was dropped.

The main purpose of the Selborne–Fisher changes was to open up the opportunities for promotion and responsibility for engineers, thus attracting men of high intelligence and powers of leadership who, Fisher believed, would direct a sometimes reluctant Navy into the era of accelerating technological revolution. Men of high calibre were, in fact, quickly attracted, although the chronology of naval engineering expertise was interrupted for a period of ten years due to the too early fading out of the current training of the old type (pre-Selborne–Fisher) engineers and the temporary interruption between 1914 and 1919 of theoretical training for the new scheme (E) officers.

With a few honourable exceptions this Fisher concept of bringing 'greasers' (as many still called them) into the main run of the Navy's officer structure was unwelcome to most senior officers in the post World War I Navy, all of whom had trained under sail and so distrusted such a radical move. Thus it was that in the 1920s the clock was put back as far as practicable and engineers, though permitted to keep the (E) after their name and the curl on their stripes, originally denoting executive status only, (and despite the fact that the Navy had originally pinched the gold stripe and so called 'executive curl' from the Customs and Excise there was much seaman opposition to such a sweetener) were once more relegated in the pecking order and their 'military' status removed or, as some would have it, their 'civilian' status in a fighting service resurrected. Inevitably they were thus deprived of most of the technological influence they might have exerted, which Fisher had understood was so essential to the shaping of Britain's future maritime weapon.

Before moving to the third great change in officer structure resultant on the lessons of World War II, it is relevant to mention the then current Naval arrangements whereby the appraisal of officers' performance and their opportunities for advancement were decided, as well as the fairly authoritarian rules which prevailed in the appointing of officers.

Broadly the different categories of officer were 'looked after' in their own individual groupings. Thus the gunnery school, the torpedo school and the navigation school indicated who they wished to be appointed to a ship on commissioning, and these appointments were co-ordinated by a commander known as the Naval assistant to the Second Sea Lord, who also looked after the 'salthorses' (non-specialist executive officers). The paymasters were appointed by the paymaster director general.

In the case of the engineers however such a simple solution was not acceptable. The phasing out of the old type engineer officer and the introduction of the new Selborne–Fisher scheme (E) officers was causing a considerable muddle in the training, promotion and appointing of the whole engineering branch. The old type 'engineer' entry to the RN Engineering College had ceased, and the new (E) officers had received only practical training at sea during the first war. By its end none had been trained in engineering theory and the old type engineer still ruled the design roost. It was soon after their delayed engineering theory training had started that the new (E) specialists, to their utter dismay, were stripped of the status and position the Fisher reforms envisaged. They still believed, however, that they were closer in sentiment and standing to (G)s and (T)s and (N)s than the old type engineers who held all the senior key positions at sea and at headquarters. Indeed the new (E) officer had been brought up to believe he would be interchangeable with his seamen fellow officers and many (E) officers, like their (G), (T) and (N) specialist colleagues, also had qualified for bridge watchkeeping certificates entitling them to be officer of the watch in control of a seagoing warship. All this led them to demand that their appointments, as well as appraisals and promotions, should also be supervised by the Second Sea Lord like their seamen contemporaries, and not by the Engineer in Chief who they believed, almost certainly wrongly, to favour the old type engineer.

In the current confusion, and because he was a most far-sighted and understanding man, the then reigning Engineer in Chief in the 1920s agreed. A carefully selected engineer-captain (no new scheme officer had as yet even become a commander (E)) was appointed as the *extra* Naval assistant to the Second Sea Lord for engineering personnel (known as EAP) to take over the appointing of all (old type) engineers and (E) officers of and below the rank of commander. He was also made responsible for liaison between the

Engineer in Chief and the Second Sea Lord for more senior appointments. This was a significant double step towards integrating appointments and promotions of old type engineers with the rising tide of (E)s, and also an indication that both types, despite their loss of prestige, were now within, rather than outside, the main body of officers governed by the Second Sea Lord, the Chief of Naval Personnel. This was a step not as yet even remotely contemplated for the paymasters.

The reader, conversant today with advanced and sophisticated personnel management techniques will appreciate that no such methods existed in the Navy (or indeed anywhere) until the 1950s. The Navy, like the other services, moved forward only because, during World War II, the Admiralty with unusual daring, appointed Drs Rodger and Wilson, experienced industrial psychologists, inter alia to examine and correct the officer appraisal arrangements.

Until the advent of these two very thoughtful and perceptive men, reports on officers tended to be short and often subjective. In the case of officers of the engineering branch such reports, from sea or shore establishments, were copied into large tomes, approximately $18'' \times 14'' \times 8''$ thick, by ladies whose handwriting was sometimes not of the best, as also occasionally was the writing of the reporting officer which they were copying. Thus the ultimate recording of the officer's report was not always as it should have been. It was from these tomes that promotion boards reached judgements as to who should be promoted and who not. The psychologists' massive changes, and the longer but more objective reporting forms they introduced, made such judgements far more reliable, but the effect on 'the tomes' was catastrophic, as only one page had been allowed for each officer when he entered as a cadet. With the new and more lengthy reporting arrangements this restricted space was hopelessly inadequate. However Naval casualties of old type regular engineer and (E) officers were sufficiently high in the early days of World War II for reports of those who survived to be continued on the pages of those whose names, in large copper plate lettering, had a red DD ('discharged dead') after them. The chaos, as a selection board of three very senior officers, all wishing to examine different records on different pages of a single tome, is better not imagined.

The actual appointment of officers up to 1939 was often a matter of chance although part of the drama of leaving the RN Engineering

College was to purchase (or hire) a bowler hat and 'call' on EAP to hear one's immediately future destination. In the rather more senior ranks, the 'dagger' élite, gathered around the Engineer in Chief, were reasonably static, as were those officers who had specialised in the engineering management of the dockyards. With no marriage allowance few officers below commander's rank could afford to be married; and anyway wives were rarely acknowledged as having any impact on the appointing process. It was not unusual for an officer to read of his next appointment in the *Portsmouth Evening News* or to hear of it from Gieves, the omniscient Naval tailors, some days before he received an Admiralty direction for his impending translation, at a month's notice or less, from his current post in a home based ship or training establishment via an unaccompanied passage by P & O to a ship on a far distant station, perhaps for a three year commission.

By the late 1920s/early 1930s, many of the new (E) officers were disgruntled at what they considered a betrayal of the terms under which they had opted for the (E) specialisation. The old divisions between seamen officers and 'greasers', which Fisher had tried to excise were reopening, a process which started at Dartmouth. The Navy clearly lacked up to date technology. Although with the advent of the new engineering assistant to the Second Sea Lord (EAP), engineering promotion and appointing arrangements began to improve there was still, as with officers of all specialisations, a feeling that patronage rather than merit or more than the normal measure of luck, often played too great a part in a successful officer's career.

Then war came again. By the time it ended 75% (according to Admiral Sir Patrick Brind's working party) of the officers of the executive and (E) and (S) categories, from the rank of Vice Admiral to Captains with three years seniority, were products of the Selborne-Fisher scheme. If there were lessons to be learned, as there certainly were, such men were going to see that the Navy learnt them. Some of these lessons to do with mobility and motive power have already been described. There were many other lessons, equally important, that have not been mentioned. The composition of the Naval officer corps was a matter affecting the future of the Navy in almost every area, and many of the 75%, nearly all of whom had seen war at its worst and bloodiest, were determined that there should be a bringing together of the different skills needed in maritime war, particularly those concerned with technology. Others, much younger and subjected to the old myths at Dartmouth and Eaton Hall, were less enthusiastic.

Two perceptive reports in the immediate post-war years highlighted the problem. The first was from a working party chaired by Vice Admiral, later Admiral Sir Patrick Brind, GBE, KCB; and the second by the Honourable Ewen Montague KC. The most telling part of Admiral Brind's report was as follows.

'The design and equipment of our ships and weapons and our ability to take advantage quickly of scientific and technical developments had a searching test during the war and it is felt by many officers that our standards at the beginning left much to be desired...Before the war we did not keep sufficiently close to scientific and technical affairs...the implications since 1925 and the separation of the (X) (seamen) and (E)(engineering) branches may be far reaching and need further enquiry.

The Engineer in Chief has been consistently dissatisfied with the proportion of second choice engineers...many had no real keenness or aptitude...In spite of the low standard of some of the candidates on the Special (public school) Entry the engineering branch, as a whole, with its proportion of Dartmouth and Lower deck entry, has a splendid war record in keeping our ships at sea in the face of great difficulties and dilution of personnel.'

It would be dangerous to use this argument for satisfaction with the present state of affairs, with the rapid advance of technical developments it is necessary to raise the standard of engineer officers and to create a real spirit of enthusiasm.

Meanwhile Montague approached the problem differently.

'There is clearly an impression that the Engineering Branch is at a disadvantage from the point of view of the responsibility it enjoys and of the career prospects it offers. There may be good reasons at this point in time why the Admiralty would be well advised to review the whole relationship between the two branches (X and E) as it has evolved since the Selborne scheme.'

By the early 1950s a committee under Vice Admiral Sir Aubrey Mansergh, KBE, CB, DSC* had been engaged for some months in seeking a solution to another difficult problem resulting from the run-down of the war time Navy and its changing shape, from a battleship and battlecruiser Navy to a much smaller carrier and frigate fleet. One effect of this change of pattern had been to restrict the opportunities of seagoing experience for seamen officers to well below the absolute minimum essential for sea command. As a result, Mansergh had proposed, and the Admiralty had accepted, that seamen executive officers bearing the rank of commander should be split into a 'Post List', who would continue to be given seagoing appointments, and a 'General List' of those seamen officers who would not normally receive further seagoing commands. Inevitable as this solution was, it was seen, despite fervent Admiralty denials, as the creation of a first and second XI. That was not the end of the story. General List officers (like the Post List) continued to be 'military', which meant they were entitled, with the Post List but unlike (E), (S) and electrical engineering (L) officers, to all the same marks of respect the executive seamen had collared in 1925, to have authority over all other ranks and ratings and to sit on Boards of Enquiry and Courts Martial. The remaining categories of officers, the engineers, whether mechanical, ordnance, electrical or air (many of the latter being front line pilots who had fought the Japanese over the Pacific and the Germans over France) and supply and secretariat (ex paymaster) officers, saw themselves as a third XI. Officers of the instructor and medical branches, although they were not as likely as the former to have to deal with sailors in a disciplinary way, saw themselves as a fourth XI.

At this time officer appointing and career planning, despite the new reporting procedures, were in more than the usual chaos. The post-war run down and demobilisation was in full swing and at the same time there was a degree of re-mobilisation due to the onset of the Korean war in which the Navy, like the Army, had a considerable part to play. Trooping was by sea and officers from abroad were usually 'lost' for at least 3 months' passage time and leave. It was at this moment that I was hauled out of HMS *Bermuda* to replace an officer, then the (E) appointer, who was urgently needed in a dockyard. In a way this was fortunate timing. Because I had submitted reports from the Pacific on the training and career structure for engineers which had met with some approval, I was, so I was told, going to be brought in to the appointer's office anyway, to help with the formulation of the engineering evidence to the Mansergh committee, whose next investigation was to examine the future of the (E) engineering, (L) electrical and (S) supply and secretariat officers. But this investigation was several months away and this earlier than planned appointment gave me time to learn the job and to deal with the many bitter weeds whose period of service abroad, due to the impact of another war, had been far too prolonged. But once the appointing cycle was satisfactorily re-established and after an assistant was appointed, I was sent away for a month to write up the evidence for the Mansergh committee, based on my Pacific reports.

Once this was done and submitted I returned to my appointing duties in EAP's office and also became the (E) assessor to the Mansergh committee. The (unofficial) chairman of the assessors was Commander T T Lewin DSC (later Admiral of the Fleet Lord Lewin of Greenwich, KG, GCB, LVO, DSC) then Naval assistant to the Second Sea Lord and, besides me as a representative of the Engineer in Chief, there was also an electrical (L) and a supply and secretariat (S) assessor.

This 'assessor' system was rather a good one. Assessors were briefed on the developing views of the committee and charged with reporting these accurately to their 'tribal chiefs', the Engineer in Chief, the Director General Supply and Secretariat and the Director of the Naval Electrical Division. The assessors kept each other informed of their principals' views as well as Admiral Mansergh; and were able to indicate when a personal meeting between their principal and the chairman was desirable to iron out difficult points. Thus discussion went ahead fast and amicably.

As the work progressed the strength of the opposition to a General List including engineers and supply and secretariat officers, by many vocal and rather less senior, and just a few more senior but non Selborne–Fisher scheme officers, became clear to the assessors. Indeed the Second Sea Lord Admiral the Hon Guy Russell, GBE, KCB, DSO, a staunch believer in Fisher's ideas, once showed me a second 'in' basket on his desk entirely filled with letters from retired and serving officers accusing him, as he said, of 'betraying his salt'. Commander Lewin, like Admiral Russell, was fully convinced of the need for change and sometimes endured equal obloquy with that outward calm that kept the Cabinet committee and the Prime Minister on the rails during the Falklands. As the evidence mounted, and despite the very considerable contrary pressures on them, Admiral Mansergh and his committee concluded that radical change, involving the assimilation of (E) and (S) and (L) officers into the new General List, was essential.

They laboured on the precise meaning of military command, administrative command, departmental command, qualified military status, the right to wear an executive curl, the chain of command, the need or not for different coloured cloth to indicate specialisation, the ability to command in boats and a whole avalanche of seeming minutiae that were cast at them by furious opponents of the whole idea. Nobody today should minimise the importance of the lonely furrow that the Mansergh committee ploughed or the debt the Navy owes to Admiral Russell for his determination that engineers and supply officers should join the General List, in some way or another.

In the end, the Mansergh Committee carried the day and, with the backing of the Second Sea Lord, the Board approved their proposals. There was, however, a price to be paid and when the price was made known, many of those concerned, including the assessors, who had had a hand in the committee's work, received a fair measure of 'hate' mail from both fellow engineers and supply officers.

As the need to make their solution more acceptable to the non-Post List seamen officers, already deeply upset at being relegated to a seaman General List (and now apparently to be bracketed with (E)s and (S)s and (L)s and so doubly disgruntled) became manifest, the committee felt impelled to insert a number of caveats. These vaguely implied that (E), (L) and (S) officers were incompetent as 'officers and leaders' and would have to receive coaching in (military) executive duties before being admitted to the chosen few. I had used Dean Swift's words in my evidence to the committee to describe the prevailing view of many executive officers.

We are God's chosen few,
All others will be damned.
There is no place in Heaven for you,
We can't have Heaven crammed.

The committee urged that particular attention should be devoted to ensuring that these three (at present non-General List) categories of officer were capable of exercising command in boats and over all categories of rating. This was a curious reiteration of the theme

which had so profoundly exercised the Naval staff in 1925 (*chapter 4*).
With Commander Lewin who then, and forever after, so staunchly
not only defended, but promoted the General List, Admiral
Mansergh was reminded of experience in Hong-Kong at the end of
the war when young (E) officers were in command of armed posses
of seamen seeking out marauding bandits, when it was an (E) officer
who had won the first post-war Sydney to Hobart yacht race, and
that sailing and entry into the Fastnet race was a normal RN
Engineering College pastime. He was reminded too that it was an (S)
Lieutenant, the Captain's secretary, who was almost uniquely
awarded a DSO (usually the prerogative of more senior officers) for
taking command on the bridge of HMS *Hardy* when Captain
Warburton-Lee VC was killed in the first battle of Narvik. Mansergh,
like Lewin, thoroughly understood the objections to these
derogatory paragraphs, but he and the Board also had to take
account of the large number of (mainly Dartmouth educated)
officers whose whole upbringing caused them fundamentally to
view with distaste the very idea of permitting the three erstwhile
'non-military' branches to join them in a common General List.
Meanwhile the committee of the United Service Club (the Senior)
practically went into orgasm at the thought of reversing the decision
of 1925 and allowing engineers once more to be admitted to such a
select circle—and supply officers too! However, the objections of so
many seamen officers was not the only obstacle that Admiral
Mansergh and his committee had to surmount.

Alone among the three groups to be brought onto the General
List, the (S) branch was wholly in favour. Since the 1920s they had
been providing secretaries to the Board members and were
becoming skilled and powerful Admiralty politicians, a quality
usually benignly applied they still cultivate ceaselessly. They saw
increased status within their grasp, and areas of influence far more in
keeping with their undoubted talents. Administration and
management, qualities to which, increasingly, (S) officers laid claim
as the prime exponents, were the watchwords of the 1950s. Although
neither of these particular skills needed good eyesight, (and poor
eyesight was often the cause of an enthusiastic Naval entrant
becoming an (S) officer), both skills are greatly improved by
technical literacy. (Paradoxically, Fisher believed that commissions
for paymasters should be abolished and their tasks undertaken by
stores and catering warrant officers at sea and by civilians ashore).

Later the Naval member of the Murray committee, Admiral Sir David Luce (*chapter 13*), had great difficulty in arguing the committee away from the view they wished to express in their report that, even in this increasingly legalistic world (and most (S) officers are legally well qualified), any Naval officer should be able to be a secretary to a Flag Officer, but, more importantly, technical literacy should be the sine qua non of all Naval officers without exception. This was a quality which the run of the mill (S) officer, certainly on the evidence presented later to the Murray committee, seemed reluctant to aspire to and much less to regard as essential. Anyway, in the context of the Mansergh committee, as secretaries and confidantes of Board members and Commanders in Chief, (S) officers, well briefed by their (S) 'assessor', pushed hard as Mansergh's report gestated, for acceptance of a wider General List in which they would play a significant part.

The elders of the newly formed electrical (L) branch were almost united in opposition. They believed, with justification, that the extra training implied by the offensive caveats and the need to qualify 'as a military officer' would interfere with the engineering profess-ionalism so badly needed by the Navy, which the recently approved training for electrical officer entrants at Cambridge was meant to provide.

The views of the ten serving Rear-Admirals (E) or Engineer Rear-Admirals were evenly split and the proposed 'military officer' qualifying training disgusted them all. Several also strongly backed the views of the (L) Branch, and felt that a professional engineering training allied to sea experience, on which the war had shown the Navy must increasingly come to depend, would be severely reduced by the need for achieving 'qualified officer status' as apparently interpreted by the seamen. Happily for the Navy, because the Board would never have imposed the General List against the views of so many seamen officers *and* of the two professional engineering branches, however hard their (S) secretaries might press them, Vice Admiral (E) Sir Frank Mason, a marine engineering specialist who had converted to ordnance engineering was now Engineer in Chief of the Fleet. By virtue of their ordnance specialisation, officers such as Mason were full members of the officers' mess of HMS *Excellent*, the Naval gunnery school from where many of the Navy's most influential officers had come. Admiral Mason knew them all and, more important, was known and respected as a man who put loyalty

Vice Admiral Sir Frank Mason, KCB
(photograph courtesy Lady Mason).

to the Navy above parochial (E) interests. He was also a close friend and contemporary of the Second Sea Lord, as was Rear-Admiral Sydney Brown the reigning EAP. There was therefore a unique personal and professional trust between Mason and Brown and the Board. Mason committed the (E) Branch to the General List and carried with him those of his ten admirals who had been hesitant. The (L) Branch, feeling they could not be left out in the cold, reluctantly accepted the proposals also.

Mansergh put the Navy back on Fisher's road but he and his committee sensed that Fisher's phrase 'community of knowledge' might once more arouse the passions of the anti-Fisher school, so on the inspired suggestion of the (S) assessor, Commander (S) later Rear-Admiral Colin Dunlop CB, CBE, DL, Mansergh substituted Drake's (perhaps even more appropriate) words after Doughty's execution. 'I must have the gentleman to haul and draw with the mariner, and the mariner with the gentleman. *Let us show ourselves all to be of a company.*' Though Mansergh showed the way, there were still many who were reluctant to tread the all of one company path; not all were seamen officers by any means.

It was Mason's understanding of the rocks ahead, and because I had been in the thick of the Mansergh battles, that caused him to send me as second in command of the Royal Naval Engineering

Colleges at Manadon and (still) Keyham. His remit to me was to put over the new ideas and the increased responsibilities that the General List implied for (E) officers, despite the obnoxious phraseology with which the new General List had been launched.

So the General List of officers was formed and Admiralty Fleet Order 1/56 bringing it into force marked a move towards Fisher's vision of some community of knowledge and a lifelong community of sentiment between engineers and non-engineers, of a less conservative and more technically inclined Navy, as well as a turning away from a unhealthy and divisive tradition stretching back into the Middle Ages.

Nevertheless even then all was not plain sailing, as was made clear by Vice Admiral Sir Frank Mason in his valedictory message (appendix) to the Board. His influence, aided always by the wisdom of his colleagues, Vice Admiral (S) Sir Maurice Elliott and Rear-Admiral (L) Sir Kenyon Peard, did much to set the officer corps into a mould from which greater war fighting efficiency must inevitably emerge.

.

Chapter 12
The Royal Naval Engineering Colleges

Manadon and Keyham 1955–1957

The land of scholars, and the nurse of arms

The Traveller
Oliver Goldsmith

If the seaman branch of the Navy was doubly upset at the introduction of the division of seamen officers into Post and General Lists (*chapter 11*) and even more at the 'non-executive' categories of (E), (L) and (S) officers being included in the latter, they were not alone. The elders of the newly formed Electrical Branch (L) were not enthusiastic at the implications, although the hotch-potch of newly enrolled ex torpedo officers, RNVR electrical officers (turned RN), ex warrant electrical officers and civilians from the department of electrical engineering, all now with regular commissions in the RN, were less hesitant. Happily, the new Cambridge entrants who I had garnered from the schools to which I lectured while I was estranged from the Engineer in Chief, still knew nothing of Naval politics.

At the Royal Naval Engineering Colleges (RNECs) at Keyham and at Manadon outside Plymouth, matters were even less happy. There were a number of reasons for this, and the implications of the Mansergh committee (*chapter 11*) were not, prima facie, the main cause; although as other difficulties were alleviated Mansergh gradually worked its way to the top of the moan list.

If Dartmouth was the cradle of the Navy and had survived its wartime migration to Eaton Hall in Cheshire (although the anti-engineering bias seemed to have increased) the RN Engineering College at Keyham had been the cradle of the Engineering Branch for nearly 100 years. Now, in the mid 1950s the new college at Manadon was beginning to usurp the Keyham magic. This new college was the result of decisions by a Board of Admiralty composed of war

The Royal Naval Engineering College at Keyham (photograph courtesy RNEC).

experienced senior officers who had been young men in the pre-World War I Fisher era. Unlike their Board predecessors in the 1920s, they realised that technology had to be the life blood of the new and smaller Navy which they must quickly create, and they were sadly aware that their predecessors' actions in the 1920s had robbed the Navy of much of the new technology that Germany had demonstrably possessed in 1939. They had also learnt from the US navy's great maritime campaign in the Pacific how mobility had been brought to a pitch that the Royal Navy should have achieved, but in fact had not even aspired to, and that this failure was due to the pre-war casting aside of Fisher's doctrines. They had begun to see, albeit at first dimly, that Fisher's philosophy, some community of knowledge and a lifelong community of sentiment, was the right one and that some community of knowledge meant in practical terms, that all Naval officers, those on deck the future captains of war, must have a general background knowledge of engineering applicable to the weapons (in which propulsion machinery was just one) with which they would have to fight. Further, if the new Navy was to be designed and built on the post-war basis of galloping technology, then there must be a sea-experienced core of officers trained to the highest professional engineering standards who could be used as interpreters. Only by possessing such a core of qualified interpreters could the activities of pure and applied scientists and engineers in the civil sector, the articulate high priests of new and accelerating technology, be directed towards the daunting practicalities of war at sea, so different to those in which the latter normally moved, or indeed to other types of conflict.

Admiral Sir Aubrey Mansergh's committee did more than create a new Naval officer structure, it spelt the end of the distaste by the above deck officer for the below deck engineers. The committee recommended, and the Board of Admiralty approved that the officer corps, deck officers, graduate engineers, supply officers and eventually all officers, must come to regard themselves as 'all of one company', in Drake's words; something that manifestly had never before been the case. A series of exceptionally wise Boards of Admiralty, with an eye to the future, not only re-established the Fisher philosophy but also saw that a nationally recognised Naval engineering training establishment, to which (as endorsed by Lord Murray's subsequent committee, *chapter 13*) all officers should go for engineering training to a greater or lesser extent as required by their roles in the whole Naval affair, was an essential which only the embryonic Manadon could supply. So, the Royal Naval Engineering College at Manadon, conceived in the immediate pre-war period, when the lack of naval engineering expertise and the lack of influence of naval engineers on machinery and weapons had been first recognised, gestating slowly throughout World War II and its immediate aftermath, was given the 'go-ahead' immediately after Mansergh's recommendations were approved. Such approval carried with it the stipulation that Manadon should not look on its role only as the college of naval engineering for engineers but should also move towards a wider role embracing eventually some engineering training for all Naval officers. Though, for traditions sake, it was still called a 'college', it was visualised as a university, in that training would be universal for all officers, though to varying degrees. Additionally, because except for their early days at

Dartmouth, it would be the one Naval establishment where all Naval officers at one time or another would go, it would provide the cement binding the Naval officer corps together in a community of sentiment (Fisher's words) to an extent that had never before been attempted since the Selborne–Fisher scheme. The scheme in fact, in an updated version, the Mansergh recommendations had just endorsed.

A decade had passed since the end of the war by the time the Mansergh committee recommendations, coming on top of a previous but related review by Admiral Sir Patrick Brind and another by the Hon Ewen Montague KC, were approved and the pattern of the new fleet and the Navy's officer corps was beginning to emerge (and Treasury approval for the full implementation of the Manadon project had been received). This period had not been a happy time for the Keyham/Manadon combined College. Administration was difficult between two separated and rather hostile communities, the syllabus was being constantly reviewed and worst of all, as described later, the entry standards of all Naval officer candidates, except the newly forming Electrical Branch (for the moment destined for Cambridge), had ill-advisedly been reduced by the Admiralty because of the post-war drop in recruiting.

In addition both Dartmouth and Keyham/Manadon were suffering from an ill-conceived but well meant Admiralty directive, which had coincided with the demise of the Naval officer entry for 16 year olds. It ordered the colleges, 'as far as possible to be run on university lines'. The origin was probably a sincere attempt to abolish some of the worst and most childish elements of the Dartmouth regime for 13 year olds (described in *The Man Around the Engine*) carried forward into the 16 year old entry. The immediate effect of this directive had been to cause a drop in the moral and personal standards of behaviour amongst some (but happily for the Navy only some) new officer entrants, possibly tolerable on a civilian campus which the concept was presumably meant to emulate, but out of place in a Naval training establishment educating officers as engineers, and training them in the art of dealing with human nature, which is the art of Naval command and leadership. At Dartmouth and Keyham/Manadon, both Captains were agreed, regimes of extraordinary laxity had evolved, with no noticeable increase in intellectual vitality.

At Manadon, lectures by young uniformed instructor officers, most of whom had never seen a ship, were unpunctually attended. They had been given powers of academic type punishment, but these were pointedly ignored by officers under training who had already been to sea and, indeed, were senior to their instructors. In the old days Keyham had boasted only one married officer (and that a shot gun wedding) among the officers under training. Wartime and marriage allowances had changed all that, but not the strong pressure currently exerted by the authorities, bred in the old tradition, to discourage and if possible to stop officers marrying. This Canutism caused distress and ill will, while failing to hold back the matrimonial tide and generally encouraging less savoury habits. Married officers were permitted to live in Plymouth, a further inducement to marriage in view of the over-heated or icy, one breeze block thick, temporary hutments and the temporary wartime and rather insanitary eating arrangements. Daily parades and early morning physical training, such as had always graced the monastic life of pre-war Keyham, were still part of the routine. Not bad, it can be argued, but activities which led to much ill-feeling amongst the more mature, married, and therefore in the early mornings sometimes rather exhausted young officers, and so were of little practical disciplinary use. Saturday all night leave was permitted for all. Paradoxically, formal Sunday parades were compulsory only for those in the College. Inevitably the married officers' homes became weekend hostels and strange rookeries were rented where bachelors could sleep or pursue their particular delights. Sunday parades were sparsely attended and church congregations were confined mainly to the staff as the kindly chaplain, although a world authority on the Venerable Bede, failed to attract materially minded and virile adolescents. A few who saw a place for things of the spirit preferred to sit at the feet of a splendid vicar in Plymouth, thereby depriving the College of their example, although it should be said that one of these eventually took Holy Orders and returned to the College as a very effective Chaplain; another placed a chamber pot on the top of the College spire from where, with the very greatest difficulty it was removed by the brave Plymouth Fire Brigade. In reality, Naval officer training from new entry onwards was an ill regulated, misdirected, unimaginative, hotch-potch, for which the Admiralty, rather than the loyal commanding officers and staffs at Dartmouth and Manadon/Keyham, was entirely responsible.

Officer recruitment was dropping steadily and in a futile attempt to improve it, the academic entry requirements had been lowered some time before, despite protests, particularly from the Engineer in Chief. Apart from the Electrical Branch entry at university level, which was bravely maintained by the Branch's founding fathers, Dartmouth candidates, some of whom would eventually reach Manadon, were by the mid 1950s permitted to make three attempts between the ages of 17 and 18, at an examination, part of which was only at O level standard and part at O level plus one year. In plain terms those candidates who were one to two years behind the average schoolboy's attainment of these academic levels at grammar and public schools, would still stand a good chance of entering the Navy. Schoolmasters saw little future for their best boys if the Navy needed only the less intellectually endowed and so gave up recommending it as a career.

During my time as a lecturer recruiting for the new Electrical (L) Branch, Mr Hallward, then Headmaster of Clifton College, had permitted me to report to the Admiralty his actual words to me on the subject of careers in the Navy.

'You ask that some of our best boys should join the Navy as executive officers and go to the top. Then, quite deliberately, you deny them any tertiary education in order to inculcate them with two mysterious qualities—leadership and seamanship. If you selected them properly in the first place then academic quality and leadership should already be there and should only need fostering. Seamanship, like anything else if the patient is willing, can be learned as a spare time occupation. Two thirds of these, often our best boys, you then throw out at 45 with no trade and no profession—but wonderful manners. You ask about engineers. To these I readily concede you give one of the best technological educations in the country. But after the age of 40 you deny all of them any chance of fulfilling themselves in their vocation. As a result you have a frustrated and often bitter crowd of men, most of them itching to leave the Navy for industry, where they are so very welcome. I would never actively discourage a boy who was set on the Navy. But I would never encourage the waverer.'

If many cadets were far ahead of the minimum standard, some were not, and so a disproportionate time had to be spent at Dartmouth cramming the backward cadets (and later at Manadon, the backward midshipmen/sub-lieutenants) while the brighter ones marked time academically. This extraordinary lapse by the Admiralty into an abysmally low academic entry standard permitted even more than the usual percentage of engineering artificers, who have always contributed so much to the Engineering Branch, to qualify as cadets for Dartmouth. In far too many cases the requirements of the engineering syllabus at Manadon, strictly sustained to professional standards by the Institution of Mechanical Engineers, subsequently defeated them. As there was no way back to artificer they had to leave the Navy, whereas had they stayed as artificers many of them, through personality and practical skills, would have achieved what used to be called Warrant rank (and had now moved through the term 'Branch officer' to 'Special Duties officer'). They and the Navy were the losers.

In the Mansergh committee report the clause about exercising command in boats was clearly regarded as critical to the future of the combined General List. This had disturbed many seamen officers who believed that (E) or (S) or (L) officers were incapable of such a feat and it disturbed many of the latter categories even more for they knew very well that they were perfectly capable. Anyway the problem was quickly dealt with under a well known and greatly admired 'salthorse' commander at Dartmouth (later Rear-Admiral Geordie Leslie, CB) who, in the years ahead and despite the appalling weather around Iceland, by sheer leadership and seamanship, both learnt in desperate wartime Atlantic convoy battles, was to win the 'cod war' against that country, with a squadron of our smallest frigates. Dartmouth's boatwork had always been a major part of the curriculum and Geordie ensured it remained so. At Manadon, besides dispatching Lieutenant (E) Michael Bailes to make the first solo voyage to New Zealand in his 25 ft Folkboat, most young officers sailed either in Admiralty provided yachts, in a Dragon class yacht bought by the mess or in their own smaller boats.

Ocean sailing was not the only character forming avenue the RNEC pursued. Young (E) officers were exposed to the rigours of 'officer of the day' in the barracks, where they could sample some of the seedier chapters of Naval life. Rear-Admiral (E) Desmond Hoare (an instigator of Outward Bound for the Services or, as it is now known, 'adventurous training') had recently become Headmaster of Atlantic College at St Donat's, the first of the United World Colleges.

Obviously Manadon, his engineering alma mater, had to follow his lead and so groups of officers spent one or two weeks in the worst of weather in the Cairngorms or Glencoe under the distant supervision of their own staff officers. Those who showed competence, courage and leadership under arduous conditions were then permitted to lead expeditions of young artificers and stokers (now more aptly renamed engineering mechanics) on similar physically trying and often hazardous expeditions. All officers spent a week at HMS *Raleigh*, the Naval new entry training establishment, to see at first hand how young men from civilian life were turned into sailors. There they would experience the problems of motivating raw recruits before the imprint of Naval discipline had begun to make itself felt. The more senior amongst the officers under training were made responsible for the good order of their individual messes and for the whole daily routine and security at Manadon outside working hours. As regards attending lectures it was made clear that each officer was responsible for his punctual attendance at his place of duty. Unpunctuality for instruction was severely dealt with as an offence against Naval rather than academic discipline. Finally it was accepted that Manadon/Keyham was not a university in the civilian sense of the word but a training establishment under strict Naval discipline from Monday until midday Saturday. At weekends, within civilised bounds, the officers under training were encouraged to regard the College as their home. Apart from rostered duties there was no leave restriction and no parades to be avoided by sleeping out on someone's sofa. The Manadon hutments if not up to the Ritz, were rent free and breakfast was there for the eating. The rookeries withered; hangovers diminished and church attendance, with a new and extrovert Naval chaplain 'Parson' Marson, marginally improved.

From 1956 onwards the new Mess at Manadon started to take shape and, somewhat belatedly, after nearly half of the first stage had been built, the First Sea Lord, AF the Earl Mountbatten and the Countess Mountbatten, met by an armed guard of young (E) officers under training from thirteen nations laid the foundation stone amidst considerable pomp. Meanwhile great progress had been made in extending the Manadon instructional block and much of the working day was moved from Keyham. Her Majesty the Queen declared the College open, and at a later stage, His Royal Highness,

The foundation stone laying ceremony at the Royal Naval Engineering College, Manadon (photograph courtesy RNEC).

Aerial view of Manadon (photograph courtesy RNEC).

The Prince of Wales opened further important instructional and residential buildings.

Gradually the offensive paragraphs in the Mansergh scheme were forgotten and a more philosophical approach to the role of engineering officers began to evolve. In a number of lectures the more senior officers under training, soon to graduate and go to sea as professional engineers, were given details of the international situation from which Britain's defence stance derived, and from that basis the role of the Navy and the role of (E) officers within the Navy, first as junior officers at sea and then in the more senior posts responsible for machinery, weapon and aircraft design and maintenance. Perhaps an extract from just one of the lectures will help to reveal the main responsibilities of naval engineers, as engineers in the 1950s then saw them, for which the Royal Naval Engineering College, amongst its other broader roles, was there to train them.

'If the Navy is to maintain its traditional place as an up to date and effective fighting weapon then it must retain the closest relationship with technological progress and development in the world. In the Navy the responsibility for this relationship both technically and in the field of human relations (rendered so complex by technical achievement) is becoming more and more the responsibility of the engineer. Naval engineers are the plank between the Navy and industry over which a two-way traffic of Naval requirements and technical achievements must flow. One of the engineer's jobs when he reaches the Admiralty is to ensure that the scientist's dreams, always so expensive and always so alluring to the non-technical officers, are not allowed to develop to the point where the statesman's weapon, the Navy, is imperilled by a great outpouring of treasure straining at the gnat of perfection. At the Engineering Experiment Station in Annapolis, Maryland, USA, there are, over the door these words, which to some extent sum up the role of any naval engineer.

> 'The work it is intended to do will never be completed. There will always be progress and it is the work of the Experiment Station to assist in determining what is progress—and what is not.'

The main function of technical officers therefore is to ensure that all modern scientific discoveries are fully explored and those that are judged as likely to be of potential use to the Navy, and can be developed within the resources available or that might be made available, are selected. With this must go an understanding of the human problems that the use of such developments in Naval warfare may promote. To sum up,

1. The engineering officer must be professionally accepted by industry.

2. The engineering officer must be fully seized of Naval operational constraints and must be able to speak to industry and scientists with that complete assurance that can come only from seagoing experience.

3. Fortitude has been defined as 'grace under pressure'. Nowhere is the pressure greater than on those below the waterline who know little of what is happening in battle. The engineering officer must have qualities of leadership which will enable him to inspire men in battle with fortitude; as well as the rather different type of leadership that will enable him to point scientists and industry towards the wide variety of machinery and weapons the Navy needs.

And lastly discipline. Here Admiral of the Fleet Lord Jellicoe speaks. In a consideration of the question of discipline one is, in these days, at once brought face to face with the prevailing spirit of the times. This spirit is roughly described as 'democracy', but to a large extent it means a disinclination to accept any form of restraint and a desire for unrestricted freedom of life and action. From the point of view of the State this attitude of mind is regrettable and may be dangerous. In the Naval service such an attitude to discipline is quite incompatible either with efficiency in general or the well being of a particular unit. What does the Navy gain by discipline? First it engenders a spirit of calmness in emergency—the same spirit that keeps a disciplined man at his post when all his comrades have fallen, will keep a man cool in the midst of emergency, panic and disaster. In other words discipline renders a man more capable of facing the chances and changes of human existence. Secondly, discipline produces a certain determination and firmness of character. A disciplined man who has been given a difficult task to accomplish is more likely to carry it through than the undisciplined man who may be turned aside at the first obstacle. The man of discipline has learnt to resist, to bear up, to hold on, in spite of all difficulties. Discipline teaches sentiments of confidence and self respect for having learnt to obey a man has gone a long way to learning to command. In a word the object and result of true discipline is to inspire men with bravery, firmness, patience, self respect and with a sentiment of honour.

Lastly, as an engineer, you must surely cultivate a sense of humour. Never forget that you can buy a man's time, you can buy a man's physical presence at a given place; you can even buy a measured number of skilled muscular motions per hour per day. But you cannot buy enthusiasm; you cannot buy initiative; you cannot buy devotion of hearts and minds and souls. You have to earn these things.'

The impact of all the 'officer' training, called for by the requirements of the new General List and a determination that (E) officers should show the way to the Navy in officer-like qualities, tended to restrict engineering instruction time. This made the problems of those young officers whose intellectual abilities failed to cope with the syllabus even more insurmountable. With only a few medium or really high flyers the situation was extremely difficult, and it was only through the understanding of two successive Deans, Instructor-Captains P W B Taylor and A J Bellamy later Rear-Admiral Bellamy, Director of Naval Education, as well as the two directors of engineering, Commander W B S Milln (later Captain of the College) and Commander later Vice Admiral Sir Allan Trewby KCB, that time was found for these extra curricular activities within an already compressed academic programme. What was needed, all were agreed, was a higher entry standard and thus less need for cramming sessions for a sizeable group of each entry.

Outspoken submissions from Dartmouth and Manadon expressing concern for the future if the existing low academic entry standards for officers were maintained, seemed to have little or no effect. These coupled with fleet complaints about the personal standards of some young officers arriving in the Fleet, and a remarkably powerful valedictory message to the Board (*appendix*) together with his views on the diminishing academic entry standards and the regime at Dartmouth, from the Engineer in Chief of the Fleet, Vice Admiral Sir Frank Mason KCB, caused the First Sea Lord, Lord Mountbatten and the First Lord, the Earl of Selkirk, to chivy a reluctant Admiralty into action. This was despite despairing cries of those backing the original (bogus) 'university' idea that 'it was too early to uproot the young plant'.

I had recently been selected for promotion to captain and was therefore to be relieved from my post as second in command of the combined engineering colleges. In no time at all I was translated to a bathroom adjoining the small office in the old Queen Anne's Mansions which, as an appointer and assessor to Mansergh, I had left only 30 months earlier. There I was told to research entry standards and basic officer training and produce, within three months, a memorandum informing the Board of Admiralty of what seemed to be wrong. If approved, this would be used as a briefing statement for a powerful, mainly civilian, committee, which Lord Selkirk had in mind to undertake the task of recommending the changes that should be made to the academic entry standards of officers, as well as to their subsequent early Naval training.

Chapter 13
The Entry and Training of Naval Officers

The Murray Committee 1958

In the end it's brains that count.

Vice Admiral Sir Aubrey Mansergh to the author, 1954

We don't want brains, we want leaders.

Witness to the Murray Committee, 1958

The mounting wave of criticism (*chapter 12*) flowing back into the Admiralty, of the personal standards, intelligence, outlook and leadership qualities of what in fact was only a small proportion of the young officers joining the fleet, once started, became a flood. Both the First Sea Lord and the First Lord were determined that radical and urgent steps should be taken to correct a problem which, otherwise, would haunt the Navy for decades ahead. My post-Manadon leave curtailed, I was promised first three months, subsequently reduced to two, to complete my research and compile an aide memoire for the Board. I was fortunate that some of the work had already been completed when I had been one of those consulted by Admiral Sir Frank Mason when he compiled a memorandum for the Board of Admiralty on the standard of Naval officer entry and the Dartmouth training. In the end I turned out a turgid eight page report with fifty pages of appendices.

Appendices A to D dealt with the Navy's need for leaders, technical training for *all* officers, for Mansergh's 'all of one company' attitude to be indoctrinated from the start and fully professional engineering training for only a *proportion* of officers.

Appendix E described Naval entry since the 13-year-old entry was abandoned, how the best brains in public schools were being pushed

towards classics, and the Admiralty's need to extend its officer
recruiting into the the secondary schools in the Midlands and
northwards, where engineering was considered a much more
acceptable profession.

Appendix F detailed statistics of the drop in officer recruiting over
the previous decade.

Appendix G attempted to refute the idea that engineering
expertise and good leadership were incompatible.

Appendix H exposed the grossly uneconomic use of Dartmouth's
training facilities and the over payment of cadets and midshipmen.

Appendix J attempted to summarise the qualities required of
future Naval officers.

Appendix K summarised the existing officer training.

Appendix L detailed the existing low academic entry regulations.

Appendix M summarised criticisms both from sea and the
Engineer in Chief.

Having defined the situation, the aide memoire then proposed
certain changes and their justification in six further appendices.

Appendix N summarised the more radical changes proposed.

Appendix O compared the proposals in Appendix N with the
arrangements in force at Dartmouth and the US Naval Academy,
Annapolis.

Appendix P detailed the views of those who argued that all
officers should start as ratings.

Appendix Q suggested a discipline appropriate to Dartmouth and
Manadon, excoriated the 'university idea' and stressed that the
young Dartmouth entrants were on probation and that their conduct
had to show they were likely to be acceptable to the Navy in their
behaviour, bearing and attitude to hard work.

Appendix R suggested leadership training with a Christian
background and how the Navy should start to confront marxist
doctrines.

Sir Keith Murray (now Lord Murray of Newhaven) then
chairman of the university grants committee and lately Rector of
Lincoln College, Oxford, had told the First Lord that he would accept
the committee's chairmanship with, as members, Rear-Admiral J D
Luce CB, DSO*, OBE, Naval Secretary to the First Lord; Mr Nigel

The Murray committe; (l–r) David Dell, Rear-Admiral Luce, Sir Keith Murray, Nigel Abercrombie, Sir Willis Jackson, Professor Allen and the author (photograph author's collection).

Abercrombie, Under Secretary, Naval Personnel (later Sir Nigel Abercrombie, Secretary General of the Arts Council); Sir Willis Jackson FRS, research director, English Electric (later Professor Lord Willis Jackson) and Professor Alan (later Lord) Bullock.

After the first meeting Alan Bullock fell ill and resigned. His place was taken by Professor Harry Allen MC, then director of the Institute for United States Studies and now professor emeritus and Dean of the school of English and American studies, University of East Anglia. My appointment as assistant engineer in chief (personnel) was postponed and I became the committee's staff officer. Mr David Dell, then an Admiralty Resident Clerk and now a deputy secretary in the department of Trade and Industry, was appointed as secretary, subsequently to delight the committee with his elegant prose.

Submarine specialists such as Admirals Fieldhouse, Grantham, Hezlet, Hutchinson, Luce, Mackenzie, McGeoch, Raikes, Roxburgh, Simpson, Troup and Woodward, have provided many of the top brains in the Navy and, with destroyer officers, most of the best leaders of our men in the increasingly difficult social conditions since the 1920s. Some hold that the reason for their leadership qualities lies in their wide understanding of all the different skills needed in the

Navy and their close links and obvious sympathy with the
engineering expertise which the submarine service particularly
requires. Whatever the truth one of the Navy's more curious and
ultimately self defeating aberrations is that so few submariners have
served on the Board of Admiralty and even fewer have reached the
top. Admiral Luce, the first to become First Sea Lord, felt he had to
retire due to the cancellation of the the large carrier programme just
at the start of the nuclear submarine era when he was most needed.
The next came 20 years later when Admiral Fieldhouse,
Commander-in-Chief (Fleet) conducted the Falklands operation
with Woodward, another submariner as on the spot commander.
Subsequently Fieldhouse became First Sea Lord and then Chief of
Defence Staff.

Between the wars Britain naively proposed the abolition of
submarines. This found no international favour, and from having
one of the largest submarine fleets by 1918 we went to war in 1939
with one of the smallest. In addition, without even consulting France
our ally, and forgetting the savage lesson we had learnt in World
War I, we cravenly entered into an agreement with Germany that, if
the latter deemed it necessary, she could build a submarine fleet
similar in size to that of the UK. This pernicious agreement
permitted Germany to train a core of skilled submarine commanders
before she attacked Poland in 1939 and started to build her vast
U-boat programme. Until the advent of nuclear propulsion, the
Naval hierarchy tended to shun submariners and the use of their
undoubted intellectual gifts in moulding a new Navy to suit the
times. The exercise of seapower is expensive in materiel, keeps alive
a shipbuilding industry once the glory of our nation and is becoming
increasingly economic in manpower costs. It cannot be exercised by
submarines alone, but the Navy would do well to continue to cosset
and encourage its submarine element as, in the more distant past, it
has so lamentably failed to do.

Anyway, with Luce, a famous submariner on the Murray
committee, and because I had served under (and been sunk with)
Admiral Sir Guy Grantham (another great submariner) in the war, it
was not surprising that the first business session took place in
Grantham's residence as Commander in Chief, Portsmouth. As an
old Rugbeian and Cambridge graduate Grantham could provide a
more objective view of the entry requirements than someone trained
at Dartmouth—or so I told the committee.

The committee were astonished and appalled at the prevailing low officer academic entry requirements and they all agreed that the (L) electrical branch, who had insisted on maintaining the equivalent of university entry qualifications, had set a standard to which the normal Naval entry must return. Grantham agreed with this view and also, because so many public schools still adhered to a classical education, thought that a small proportion of intellectually gifted arts entrants were acceptable provided they could demonstrate a degree of numeracy and pass a Naval exam in maths and physics.

Such a momentous escalation of the entry standards in the face of falling recruitment, but an escalation on which the committee would base all their other recommendations, required prior Board of Admiralty approval if further useful work was to proceed. So, having primed the First Lord and First Sea Lord, the committee met the Board; but so strongly had the latter been led to assume that brains and leadership were incompatible, that they were sceptical of Murray's proposals. The committee retired down, but not out.

Selkirk and Mountbatten saw a way round. The secretary and I were dispatched to produce the examination papers taken by each individual serving Naval member of the then Board when he had sat the entry exam many years before, as well as the public school common entrance exam and the Winchester college exam for the same date. These were sent to the civilian members of the committee to compare. They all agreed that the Naval entrance examination, quite apart from the stringent interview requirement, was to a much higher standard than the public school common entrance and much nearer Winchester's entry qualification. Armed with this evidence, and the fact that one particularly doubting Board member had been consistently top of his Term throughout his training at Dartmouth, the committee met the Board once more and deployed their view that 'they were trying only to restore to the Navy the same high intellectual quality that Their Lordships had exhibited so many years before'. The Board nodded their wise old heads and the committee's first hurdle was jumped!

There were other hilarious episodes. When one very senior witness thumped the table and exclaimed, 'we don't want brains we want leaders of men', it happened that at that moment I was handing round cups of tea. Inadvertently, though this was never conceded by the committee, I tripped and deposited much of the hot tea down the witness's back.

Sir Keith Murray believed that if a witness could not get his message across in 30 minutes that it was time he should leave. So sometimes, almost in the middle of a sentence of the witness's most telling rhetoric, Murray would rise and with the utmost courtesy, proffer the witness a limp handshake and thank him for his invaluable views, while the staff officer opened the door. Only once was Murray seen to hesitate. After 25 minutes of experienced testimony (for in his early years he had been a Naval cadet) by David Mathew, the Roman Catholic archbishop to the Forces, David Dell the secretary, whose sense of humour did so much to keep the committee on the right lines, passed a note via the members to the chairman which read, 'It is usual to kiss the ring of an Archbishop on his departure'. Despite some hesitation, and to the committee's disappointment, the chairman's Presbyterian upbringing prevailed and the usual limp handshake alone was provided.

The committee, now at full gallop, jumped the next two hurdles with ease. The first was the leisurely pace of the Dartmouth course and second the anomalies in the periods of study devoted to different aspects of Naval training, between Dartmouth and Annapolis.

Subject	Dartmouth	Annapolis
Science	33%	49%
Humanities	15%	24%
Professional	44%	24%
Physical/parade trg	8%	3%

The committee concluded that in the two year RN training course the contact teaching hours at Dartmouth were less than a third, rather than the half as might be assumed, of those achieved in the four year USN course at Annapolis. Worse, due to the low entry standards, a considerable proportion of the Dartmouth contact hours were spent by instructors in cramming the less well endowed. It was not the committee's task to solve these details but they strongly recommended a Board of Visitors for Dartmouth and Manadon to ensure the best use of training time, and to remedy the apparent isolation of Naval education from important countrywide trends.

The second hurdle was the much debated question of whether officers should first serve as ratings as strongly advocated by Lord Mountbatten and others. To get a feel for this the committee visited

HMS *Ganges* (sadly now no longer in existence), near Harwich, a training establishment for boy seamen and probably the most effective mechanism for turning undisciplined and often scruffy youngsters into fit and responsible young men, whose bravery, patience, firmness, patriotism and sentiments of honour not only gave the state a body of citizens who served it faithfully in the Navy but also who, on return to civil life, were a real strength to the community. The committee appreciated Mountbatten's view and that of (mostly RNVR) witnesses that a period of lower deck training was essential. But their hope was that by raising the entry standards and getting the Navy to widen its officer recruiting base, the officer entry would no longer come from any particular stratum of society. In fact, the committee saw no chance of fitting in a worthwhile period of rating training if a two year period of 'common training' for all officer specialisations was a sine qua non of the Mansergh 'all of one company' concept, in which the committee strongly believed. The only other way forward would be to revert to the 13 year old entry, to which the committee was greatly attracted, but which they had been told was politically impossible. Dell and I laboured long over the drafting of a succinct paragraph clearly defining the committee's rather nebulous views, while recalling hungrily to each other, Lord Ismay's words.

> *And when the great ones go off to their dinner,*
> *The secretary sits getting thinner and thinner.*
> *Racking his brains to record and report*
> *What he thinks, they think, they ought to have thought.*

In the end we came up with the following to which the committee thankfully subscribed.

'*The needs of the Royal Navy over the next twenty to thirty years cannot be determined precisely at the present time, but there are two clear pointers. The level of education, both general and vocational, among ratings is rising, while changes in society continuously erode the ordered class supremacy of officers. In the Navy of the future leadership is likely to come to require in addition to personality, a higher level of technological knowledge.*'

From Harwich, the committee sailed in the Dartmouth training squadron, then under the command of a very war experienced officer, Captain later Rear-Admiral Sir Morgan Morgan-Giles, DSO,

OBE, GM, MP, to Dartmouth. Professor Allen had seen a little of the Navy on the way to Normandy where, as a commando, he had won the Military Cross; Mr Abercrombie knew it well as an Admiralty civil servant; Sir Willis Jackson had been prevented from joining the Navy as a boy due to defective eyesight but, as research director of English Electric had had a hand in restoring the Navy's mobility. Sir Keith Murray, the chairman, was the only committee member without Naval experience. It was a glorious summer evening as the squadron stopped in mid-channel and the committee were transferred by whalers manned by cadets to Captain Morgan Giles' ship for dinner. Various night exercises were then carried out and later, at his own request, Sir Willis Jackson, despite his moustache, was dressed as a Naval officer to help keep watch throughout the remainder of the trip.

The magic of those hours and the splendid dinner, followed by Morgan-Giles' sage and balanced views on entry and training, enthused the whole committee. As a result they easily absorbed the outspoken views of the captain of the Royal Naval College, Captain later Rear-Admiral James Munn CB, DSO*, OBE and his training commander on the consequences of the low entry standards and the lax 'university' regime required by the Admiralty. And Munn's views were even more forcibly endorsed by Captain Sir John Walsham Bart, CB, OBE, when the committee visited the RN Engineering College at Manadon, where the education and training given was well in line with all the committee's thoughts as to how young officers should be educated and trained for Naval service.

Those who advocated training as ratings were apt also to advocate hammocks for new entry officers. Neither Admiral Luce nor I, who had slept in them as midshipmen, comprehended what personal qualities a hammock was supposed to bring to the surface. However, if there was no time to insert a period of rating training, the merits of which were debatable, the hammock situation was easier to solve and would thus, at least, show that the committee had listened to those who confessed disappointment that rating training was not possible. As a result it was suggested in one paragraph of the report that sailors' uniform should be worn for the first year of Dartmouth training and, in another, that the four large gunrooms in 'D' Block at Dartmouth should be converted into simulated ships' messdecks with sailors' mess tables, kit lockers and hammock bars. This arrangement, the committee suggested, would ensure an early and rigorous introduction to Naval communal life for the schoolboy entrant, 'so that he would be able, with the least possible delay, to take his place as a member of a disciplined service, and learn the necessity, when living at close quarters, of tidiness, order and sociability'.

As the co-drafter of that paragraph I was saddened 35 years later to find it had been disregarded.

Finally the committee foresaw great changes in society and even more in the shape of the Navy, both of which would undoubtedly recoil on Naval entry conditions and standards and the shape of future officer structures. The committee's recommendations for early training were therefore specifically framed so that they could be amended in the future without major upheaval.

In less than six months and after interviewing fifty witnesses from Admirals of the Fleet and Archbishop to national service midshipmen, receiving 63 written submissions and spending nearly two weeks in visits to training establishments, the work was complete. Briefly it recommended:

1. Raising entry standards to two 'A' level and five 'O' level passes to be taken at one sitting (those with A level passes in arts subjects would be required to take a special examination in maths and physics);

2. A common Naval training for two years ashore and afloat in the fleet for all (this would meet the Mansergh requirement, 'all of one company');

3. An academic course at university level related to whatever Naval specialisation was to be followed;

4. A Naval professional training course.

The report was signed at Pitreavie where Admiral Luce was now Flag Officer, Scotland. The Board of Admiralty read and considered it and, within two weeks, ordered that its recommendations on entry standards, routines, work load at Dartmouth and Manadon and sequence of academic, sea and technological training, should be introduced forthwith.

The Murray scheme lasted only 14 years although the same verities remain. There is talk of reviving it.

We are an island state on the ocean flank of Europe. As the old seamanship manual said,

> *'Remember that your vocation deliberately chosen is war. War as a means of peace, but still war. And in singleness of purpose for the Empire's fame, prepare for the time when the honour and welfare of that Empire may come to be in your keeping. That by your skill and valour when that time arrives you may revive the spirit and perpetuate the glory of the days...'*

Britain no longer has an empire but we live by the sea. Our farmers require 10 joules of fossil fuel energy, mostly brought from desert sands 4000 miles away, to produce just a single joule of edible energy. If we neglect the sea and its values; if penny-pinching politicians fail to provide training and resources and fail also to take advantage of advancing technology applicable uniquely to an oceanic environment, then we shall fail those whose business is on great waters, be they in the Royal Navy or the merchant navy or manning the fishing fleets. More importantly, we shall surely forfeit our survival as an independent nation.

After living with them for five months, that was my interpretation of the broad views of the intellectually powerful Murray committee, as to the future strategic needs of the UK.

Part 4 Stumbles and Triumphs on the Way Ahead

Chapter 14
The Impact of Reorganisation on the Mobility of the Fleet 1957–1961

> *In sore affliction tried by God's commands,*
> *For patience Job, a great exemplar stands:*
> *But in these days a trial more severe*
> *Had been Job's lot if God had sent him here.*

Written by Captain Marryat over the chimney piece in the room in the Admiralty where Nelson's body lay and where, until 30 years ago, captains always waited before seeing the First Lord, to be 'offered' a post. Happily habits of punctuality have improved since Marryat's day; but in 1959 the impact of some of the reorganisations of the naval officer structure and ship design arrangements were, for a time, indeed a sore affliction.

Although in 1959 the Board of Admiralty met in the lovely room where they have met for centuries (as they still do in their present incarnation as the Navy Board of the Defence Council), the Admiralty itself, inflated by war, was widely dispersed between the old Queen Anne's Mansions, where the personnel departments laboured in flats and suites and bathrooms of this, the first big residential block in London, the old Admiralty by the Horse Guards parade, sundry other London buildings and in outstations scattered around towns such as Bath. This dispersal of scarce talent did nothing to assist mutual collaboration between departments, and Admiralty and naval officer structure reorganisation nearly destroyed the newly emerging mobility (that most critical element of seapower), for which so many had worked. It happened like this.

In response to the views of war experienced (E) officers and new and more difficult staff requirements there had been a great leap forward in naval machinery design. This had involved, in the case of the numerically increasing frigate fleet designed to cross the Atlantic without refuelling, a considerable reduction in weight and space for propulsion machinery and fuel, allowing more space for weaponry and crew accomodation. These new designs were on the frontiers of marine engineering. With comparatively few production models, prototype trials were wholly uneconomic, while the urgency because of the Soviet submarine threat to the Atlantic bridge added to a thrust forward into the unknown in some design areas. Corners had to be cut. Much more refit by replacement was involved, the periodicity being derived largely from estimates of 'mean time between failure' (MTBF) of components, rather than the traditional repair on board by skilled craftsmen in space consuming workshops. All this change, in turn, implied a more advanced engineering philosophy to the one in which the majority of (E) officers, artificers, mechanicians and ratings had been trained, and with considerable foresight what was hoped would be the correct training changes had already been put in hand. Inevitably the results, good or bad, would take time to reach the fleet.

These developments had been masterminded by a series of Third Sea Lords and Controllers of the Navy responsible for materiel matters and the officer taking up this post in 1956, Admiral Sir Peter Reid, the younger son of Queen Victoria's doctor was, history may show, perhaps the most brilliant since Fisher. As flag lieutenant in HMS *Hood* to Admiral Sir William James, as a veteran of the Mediterranean battles, only just a survivor from the ill-fated ABDA command of Wavell before the fall of Singapore and as chief of staff to Admiral Sir Bernard Rawlings, the British operational commander in the Pacific, his war experience was rounded off in peace by command of a cruiser squadron, before reaching the Board of Admiralty.

The Admiralty patent with particular reference to the duties of the Third Sea Lord and Controller, still in force in the late 1950s, read as follows.

'...*AND FURTHER KNOW YE that We trusting in your wisdom and fidelity of Our especial grace DO by these Presents constitute and appoint you to be OUR COMMISSIONERS for executing the Office of OUR HIGH ADMIRAL of Our United Kingdom and of the Terri-*

tories thereto belonging and of Our High Admiral of Our Colonies during Our pleasure granting unto you or any two or more of you full power and authority to do everything which belongs to the Office of Our High Admiral as well as in and touching those things which concern Our Navy and Shipping...AND WE DO GRANT unto you or any two or more of you full power and authority to make orders for building repairing preserving fitting furnishing arming victualling and setting forth such ships vessels and fleets with all things belonging to them as to you or any two or more of you according to your best discretion shall see fit...'

Admiral Reid and his Vice-Controller, Vice Admiral Sir Nicholas Copeman, the Fourth Sea Lord, were therefore responsible for 'building, repairing, preserving, fitting, furnishing, arming and victualling the fleet and otherwise setting them forth with things belonging to them'.

Reference has already been made to some of the various design 'tribes' in Bath: the Director of Naval Construction (DNC); the Engineer in Chief of the Fleet (E in C); the Director of Electrical Engineering (DEE); the Director of Dockyards (D of D); the pool of production engineers (PE); the Director of Underwater Weapons (material) (DUW mat); the Director of Naval Equipment (DNE); the Royal Naval Scientific Service (RNSS); and the Director of Boom Defence and Salvage (DBD). It would not be true to say that the first three big and essentially 'design' departments were always at war with each other, but in each case the professional boundary was strictly manned. Any paperwork crossing the boundaries and inviting dissent always had to come for decision to the Controller, who thus supervised personally the production of ships from conception to commissioning for service, or to his Vice-Controller who dealt principally with the dockyards worldwide.

Admiral Reid determined to bring all elements of ship design, ship repair and weapons under three Directors-General who would receive their broad policy decisions and funding from the Board, but who would themselves take much of the the detailed decisions off his shoulders. With his trusted confederate and friend Sir John Lang, the Secretary of the Admiralty, they established a committee under the chairmanship of Mr Justice Nihill to test this idea and to work out the broad outlines of an organisation in accordance with Admiral Reid's concept. That Mr Justice (Sir Berkeley) Nihill was simultaneously engaged on an investigation into wild life in East Africa was seized on by many as the reason why he had been chosen for an investigation into the wild life in Bath! The fact that Nihill came up with a workable idea for the Bath fauna was rightly attributed, in large part, to the work of the committee's secretary, Mr later Sir Arthur Hockaday KCB, one of the many great Admiralty civil servants who went on to become Second Permanent Secretary in the Ministry of Defence, and, later still, vice chairman of the War Graves Commission.

The Director General (ships) (DGS), the Director General (dockyards and maintenance) (DGD & M) and the Director General (weapons) (DGW) were born. Importantly for what follows, the deputy engineer in chief who led the engineering group in Bath was absorbed into the DGS organisation with the title of Director of Marine Engineering (DME) and so was no longer answerable professionally to the Engineer in Chief of the Fleet but to the DGS, a naval constructor.

At this point it is necessary to turn to the concurrent changes in officer structure heralded by the Mansergh committee and invoked by the Board in 1956. As the General List (*chapter 12*) gradually took shape the (E) and (S) and (L) officers assumed duties and responsibilities formerly undertaken by (X) executive (but now to be known as seamen) officers; and this rearrangement started at the top. The first change, hastily undertaken by the Board because they heard that the Director of the Naval Electrical Division had the idea of becoming Electrical Engineer in Chief, was to abolish the posts of Engineer in Chief of the Fleet and the Director General, Supply and Secretariat Branch, as well as the Director of the Naval Electrical Division and, as posts formerly held by executive officers of equivalent seniority fell vacant, these officers were popped into them. This saved two Vice Admiral's and one Rear-Admiral's posts, to the delight of the Permanent Secretary and the Treasury. However it created such a hullaballoo, especially in the engineering and supply branches, that initially as a sop, but today as a requirement as advisers on professional qualifications, the honorary titles (with particular emphasis on the honorary) of Chief Naval Engineer Officer (CNEO), Supply and Secretariat (CNSS) and Electrical Officer (CNLO) were created, to be held by the senior specialist officers newly transferred into General List posts. That concession ensured that each 'tribe' retained a chieftain to look after its interests in the fair distribution of posts among the higher ranks of the Navy, as well as in the General List promotion stakes lower down the seniority ladder.

It has already been mentioned that not long before the Engineer in Chief had been given the title of Engineer in Chief of the Fleet, as a recognition that he was finally responsible to the Board of Admiralty for mobility. As such he was responsible to the First Sea Lord for ensuring that any operational requirements could be met, to the Second Sea Lord and Chief of Naval Personnel that the fleet was fully manned with technical personnel properly trained for their role, to the Third Sea Lord and Controller that machinery design, production and other materiel requirements were satisfactorily assembled and to the Fourth Sea Lord that machinery associated with propulsion and other ancillary machinery was designed and positioned and spare gear made available, so that dockyards could provide satisfactory refits.

These responsibilities the Engineer in Chief of the Fleet had exercised through three distinct lines of command. First his deputy at Bath was charged with incorporating in ships the best design of propulsion machinery and such ancillary machinery as laundries, that could be produced within the timescale and funding stipulated. Further the deputy was the first to be told by squadron or fleet engineer officers of unexpected breakdowns or cases of repeated unserviceability in the fleet, in order that he might organise whatever remedial action seemed appropriate. If the breakdown was assessed as due to bad design then the deputy E in C could himself correct the matter by reference to the appropriate 'Ship Section' of his department: if it was due to bad refitting by the dockyard then it could be taken up at once with the dockyard department and if necessary the Fourth Sea Lord. If it was due to lack of, or wrong, training then the matter would be turned over to the assistant engineer in chief (personnel) (AE in C P), (the post to which I had been appointed after the Murray committee). Under the Engineer in Chief of the Fleet, although still within the Second Sea Lord's superintendence, AE in C P was empowered to deal directly with all technical training establishments to create amendments to the syllabus of instruction; and also with the determination of quantity and quality of technical manpower in each Class of ship. If the breakdown was due to incompetence of the engineer officer of the ship concerned then a report on the matter would be forwarded to the Second Sea Lord's

engineering assistant (EAP) responsible for appointments and, if the
fault was sufficiently serious, then the Engineer in Chief would ask
that the officer concerned should be moved to a less demanding post
or disciplined. In these ways the Engineer in Chief of the Fleet had
not only the responsibility, but more important the means and direct
authority, for keeping the fleet mobile and also for constantly seeking to improve it. Now, suddenly, thanks to the decisions on the
Mansergh committee and the inauguration of the General List of officers, there was no Engineer in Chief of the Fleet and no-one else
with such authority.

As Assistant Engineer in Chief (personnel), I was still in play, as
was the engineering appointer (EAP). We both reported to the Second Sea Lord, but, as a result of the Nihill committee's
recommendations the deputy engineer in chief (the original focal
point for all matters affecting mobility) had become the Director of
Marine Engineering (DME) responsible only to the Director-General
(ships) (DGS). The latter, Mr later Sir Alfred Sims was a brilliant naval constructor and Head (tribal chief) of that galaxy of (usually)
brilliant naval architects, the Royal Corps of Naval Constructors
(RCNC). In private life he and his wife were a most charming couple
beloved by all, but once he entered his office he assumed a carapace
of defensive pomposity which his subordinates found difficult and
the shipbuilders quite baffling. In assuming his enormous responsibilities for all elements of warship design he resolutely refused to
accept any responsibility for the running fleet or any problems associated with its mobility and insisted that his DME should do no more
than translate running fleet problems, after being analysed, into better design for the *future*. As Sims saw it, if one of his directors had a
particular responsibility then, in the end, that responsibility became
his, despite his lack of knowledge of any marine engineering details
or operating procedures, and he was definitely not going to be responsible to the Board of Admiralty if a single ship failed to sail on
time or a flotilla or squadron had its mobility diminished for any reason whatever. Once a ship was accepted from the builders his
responsibilities had been fully discharged, or so Sims held.

Put simplistically, by the late 1950s, as a result of the Nihill committee and the new warship design organisation in Bath, there was
no-one, due to the disappearance of the Engineer in Chief (the post
abolished as a result of the Mansergh committee) to whom the First
Sea Lord could turn if ships failed operationally; there was no-one to

whom the Controller could turn to demand details of the failure. There was only Sims, the civilian Director-General (ships) who refused to have anything to do with the problem as being outside his remit. The Board was stymied.

To make matters worse, Sir John Lang, the Secretary of the Admiralty, quite by chance discovered that I was still an assistant engineer in chief (personnel) but that there was no Engineer in Chief to be assisted! So he dreamt up 'the personnel panel'. This consisted of individual cells of seamen (X), supply (S), electrical (L) and (E) officers. This meant that I was stripped of the prestigious title I then held and I became instead head of the engineering section of the personnel panel. We each reported to the head of the panel, a Rear-Admiral, later Sir Kenneth Buckley (an ex torpedo officer but in happy fact now an (L) specialist with an enormous sense of humour). The combined remit of the various heads of personnel panel sections was that we should coordinate all our activities, and forward any changes in training or personnel administration that might be thought necessary, via the Rear-Admiral and a senior civil servant, to the deputy chief of naval personnel (quite possibly someone with no technical knowledge) for final approval.

Previously, as assistant engineer in chief (personnel) I had been authorised to deal directly with any problems reflecting on technical manning or training. Now I had to invite the views of my (S), (L) and (X) colleagues on any training changes I wished to propose and then forward them up on paper through several tiers of technical illiterates before they could be implemented or denied. Bureaucracy had triumphed: mobility suffered.

It cannot be too strongly stressed that all this was happening when new and far more highly rated propulsion machinery, conceived to save space for more weaponry and crew and, for good reasons, never tested by prototype running to establish reliability and periodicity of likely component failure, was going to sea in operational warships.

Fortunately, to begin with, these two major Admiralty and Naval changes, excellent individually but potentially disastrous when narrowly interpreted together, coincided with a lull in political demands for naval operational activity and also with the establishment of the Ship Maintenance Authority (SMA). This was the sorting house for all ship defects and by compiling lists of these as they arose it was possible to demonstrate when a ship required either a short or long 'servicing' pause; and operators could be so informed. 'Authority' was a misnomer. The SMA was just a very useful statistical bureau. Meanwhile Sims stuck in his toes and refused all requests from the Director of Marine Engineering (lately deputy Engineer in Chief) to allow him to take action or give advice for the day to day problems of a nearly brand new fleet, with machinery designed to far more stringent requirements than had ever previously been demanded. The engineering element of the personnel panel found itself almost drowned in bureaucracy and the appointers were without guidance as to whether the problems that arose lay with professional incompetence or bad machinery or bad training.

While political requirements for fleet availability languished, matters soldiered on, but suddenly the world situation demanded a much greater availability of British warships which, at least initially, was not forthcoming; and those who had disagreed with Mansergh and the General List (and engineers in particular) raised shrill cries of distress. Some advocated the reappointment of an Engineer in Chief of the Fleet, some called for his appointment to the Board, and others required that the Controller should always be an engineer. Many of those at Bath railed against (the recently honoured) Sir Alfred Sims, unjustly asserting that his assumption of the headship of the Royal Corps of Naval Constructors always brought him down heavily in favour of the constructors rather than marine engineers when there were professional arguments. Meanwhile the Chief Naval Engineer Officer, in a very busy General List post which had nothing at all to do with engineering, had neither the time to master abstruse marine engineering problems nor the authority to argue them with Sims had he been able to.

Through all this the Controller, perhaps for too long, but out of loyalty to Sims, who he had personally selected to head up the ship department, and the enormity of whose task in bringing together the 'tribes' in Bath he well recognised, held his peace, but on the advice of his naval assistant soon due to be relieved, Captain later Vice Admiral Sir Peter Walker KCB, DSC, and against the advice of the Chief Naval Engineer Officer (in his honorary capacity as personnel adviser to the Board for senior (E) appointments) who favoured a far better engineer, Reid selected me, ex assessor on Mansergh, ex engineering appointer, ex-assistant engineer in chief, ex head of the engineering personnel panel, who had been in the thick of all the battles of the previous five years, as Walker's relief.

As I waited in the Nelson room to call on the First Lord and officially hear my future, I read Marryat's words at the head of this chapter. I quickly discovered after relieving Walker, a brilliant engineer and administrator, that for me it was a case of out of the personnel panel's frying pan into the fire of the Controller's office.

Chapter 15
Office of Third Sea Lord and Controller of the Navy 1956–1965

Admiral Sir Peter Reid GCB CVO, 1956–1961

Peter passed out first at Dartmouth, earning a generous tribute from King George Vth, Lord Stamfordham writing, 'I am commanded by the King to congratulate you and Lady Reid upon Peter's brilliant success, and to say that unfortunately His Majesty's own son Prince George occupied the opposite pole!! but His Majesty is so glad that tho' so far separated intellectually they are closely associated as friends!

Ask Sir James
Michaela Reid

The awesome and heavy responsibility carried by Admiral Sir Peter Reid and the Fourth Sea Lord, Vice Admiral Sir Nicholas Copeman, in accordance with the Board patent was described in the last chapter. More Controllers have been compelled to retire from ill-health or have died in the post than any other member of the Board of Admiralty. Admiral Reid always attributed his ability to keep up the pace the job demanded to the fact that halfway through his appointment he had had to enter hospital with a torn knee ligament, a pause that gave him the stamina to go on.

Reid's brain moved at an astonishing pace which was probably the reason he worked his way through three naval assistants, all Captains (E). His first, later Vice Admiral Sir Raymond Hawkins, a submarine specialist, became the first engineer to serve on the Board of Admiralty; the second, later Vice Admiral Sir Peter Walker, one of the most brilliant naval engineers of his era who had a well earned DSC for his leadership and example as acting chief engineer of Admiral Fraser's flagship in the battle of North Cape, later became chief naval engineer officer (CNEO). I was Reid's third assistant. Perhaps because of the controversies I engendered in the ship department (*chapters 16 and 17*) I was sent away to America as naval attaché. I then became Director-General of Intelligence over all three service intelligence departments and the scientific and technical and economic echelons of the Joint Intelligence Bureau. These had been combined into the Defence Intelligence Staff (DIS) by Lord Mountbatten in 1964–65.

Sir Peter Reid's personal staff was small. It was presided over by a captain of the Supply and Secretariat branch, later Rear-Admiral Sir Anthony Woodifield, who had been Reid's secretary for twelve years and was almost in telepathic communication with him. He had a Lieutenant-Commander (S) assistant. The post I inherited as the naval assistant was of captain's rank, and there was a civil servant and a stenographer. Later, when the number of ships building demanded, Reid brought in a seaman commander to establish an information room for use by the naval staff.

In the late 1950s and early 1960s the business of Admiralty was conducted on the docket system in which every comment was enclosed for all to read. Although often thought of as slow, some would say it was far more effective than the blizzard of loose minutes which copying machines have bequeathed on the Defence Ministry. Traditionally the Admiralty had the pick of the home civil service entry who, aware that the Navy would be their lifetime interest, invariably served with devoted skill. Broken only by quite frequent and always hectic Friday to Tuesday forays, accompanied by his naval assistant and the Director of Naval Equipment to prod the Clyde, Newcastle, Liverpool, Belfast and Barrow shipyards, or a day with the design departments at Bath (with the same aim) Reid's routine was invariable. After arriving at nine in the morning on the dot, he required enough dockets to be ready to keep him busy until 1030, when he saw his secretary and naval assistant to discuss the day's business. He worked standing at a reading desk and tended to deplore those of his colleagues who sat hunched up gazing at a pile of papers. Meetings with various officials or shipbuilders, with the secretary or his naval assistant taking notes, went on till a short lunch break, followed by much the same routine in the afternoon, until six in the evening when, with a 'box' of non-confidential matter Reid returned home. No docket, unless of exceptional complexity, was permitted

Admiral Sir Peter Reid (Third Sea Lord and Controller, 1956–1961, Sir Alfred Sims, Director General (ships), and Admiral Sir Caspar John, First Sea Lord 1960–1963 (photograph author's collection).

to loiter in the office for more than 24 hours. To keep up with the pace Reid set, the office worked a steady 12 hour stint from eight to eight often six days a week.

Soon after I joined the office, Admiral Sir Caspar John succeeded to the post of First Sea Lord, Admiral Sir Charles Lambe having died from a heart attack. This leadership change gave Admiral Cabanier, who had fought with Britain throughout the war and was now head of the French Navy, an excuse to come over and call on Sir Caspar and the First Lord, Lord Carrington, as a most courteous move to bring the two navies closer and to erase memories of Oran. An official call of this nature had to be returned and Lord Carrington and his wife, accompanied by the flag lieutenant to the Board, Lieutenant-Commander Holdsworth and Carrington's private secretary Mr Alastair Jaffray, together with the Controller and his naval assistant, were ferried over in an Air France aircraft for a week of hectic entertainment and interesting visits to Paris, Toulon, St Tropez (torpedo range only) and, lastly, Brest.

The generous and magnificent hospitality such as only France can provide, starting with champagne in the Air France aircraft early in the morning and an official Dinner with M. Messmer, the Minister of Defence, till late in the evening, gave all the visitors severe tummy upsets. Happily, John Holdsworth and I had brought supplies of strepto-triad but Reid's remark, 'Isn't abroad bloody, Louis', caused Captain Compston, the British naval attache who had done so much to make the visit the success it certainly was, great pain!

Our French hosts seemed anxious to forget and forgive, with one exception who took me (as I had served in HMS *Hood*) to see one of *Hood's* shells which had hit and failed to explode at Oran and which was now enshrined in a glass case outside the wardroom. Lord Carrington and his wife were fluent French speakers and the party floated on a sea of champagne and good fellowship. Admiral Reid (Le troisieme Lord de La Mer, as the French papers described him) had ordered HMS *Rhyl* to Brest to take the group home. The farewell cocktail party onboard on the last evening was made memorable by a conversation between Admiral Jubelin, the Port Admiral and our host in Brest, and Lord Carrington. Carrington, a famous and much decorated ex-Grenadier was explaining to the exceptionally tall and very well built French Admiral that he was a bit worried at the weather forecast of a force ten gale. 'However', Carrington said, 'John Holdsworth has some pills and I hope the First Lord of the Admiralty will not be seen to succumb in front of the sailors'. 'No, no, no', roared Jubelin, towering over Carrington. "'Peels' are no good. Let me 'geeve' you a 'suppositree''.

Rhyl sailed wearing the Lord High Admiral's flag because a fully constituted quorum of the Board of Admiralty, two members and a secretary (Mr Jaffray), were on board, historically the last time such an event has occurred. In the reorganisation of the Ministry of Defence, the 'commissioners for executing the office of High Admiral' have disappeared and Queen Elizabeth II herself once more holds that office. Happily, the honour of the Grenadiers was preserved and the First Lord, without any medical assistance, enjoyed the very rough trip as much as Admiral Reid.

Reid's controllership was notable for many prescient decisions besides his personal interest in the management and effectiveness of the different shipyards of the 14 strong warship group. His yardstick was interesting. If he was treated to a minimal lunch in the shipyard all was well. Full blown lunches with wine and port were regarded

Admiral Sir Peter Reid 'prodding' a shipyard. (L–r) Author, Sir Charles Dunphie (Chairman of Vickers), Admiral Reid, Mr Redshaw (Managing Director), and bowler hatted shipyard and engineering managers (photograph author's collection).

sceptically. Proceeding at a steady trot round the yard, pursued by his naval assistant and a bevy of sweating bowler hatted shipyard officials, Reid led the inspection. A fan wrongly placed here, a valve so sited that it could not easily be worked there, Reid's eye for detail missed nothing, and each criticism was reinforced by a letter to the chairman of the shipyard concerned on Reid's return to office.

Against the opinions of many scientific and strategic experts, the Controller insisted that the County class destroyers (designed to deploy Seaslug, the Navy's first anti-aircraft missile, which could also be used in a surface to surface mode) should also be fitted with guns. He insisted that in limited non-nuclear war, which he envisaged as the most likely, the ability to bombard would always be needed. The Falklands proved him right, and the 'experts' wrong.

Four of the County class destroyers were laid down and three launched during his Controllership, as were all seven of the Tribal class fitted with a Wasp helicopter and Seacat missile. Like the Counties, the Tribals were propelled by steam with a gas turbine boost for high speed. Additionally Reid saw completed three Salisbury and the two Leopard class diesel frigates and two Whitbys and three Blackwoods already building when he assumed office. As he speeded up the programme, 11 submarines were completed and nine of the steam driven Rothesay class laid down and completed, together with 20 minehunters and sweepers. He hoped too for a future for hovercraft and was one of the first to ride the Vickers prototype in the Solent. Never, in peacetime since Fisher, had so much been spent on the Navy; that it should be well spent was Reid's constant demand and personal endeavour.

As chief of staff to Admiral Sir Bernard Rawlings, Reid had seen the need for mobility and this had made him aware of the British Pacific fleet's pathetic showing compared to the US navy. The engineering 'revolutionaries' at Bath, seeking better and more economic forms of propulsion, and the Yarrow–Admiralty Research Department (YARD), both found in Reid an understanding listener and a great supporter of their ideas for the future.

Chapter 14 mentioned the changes that Reid had introduced by merging the three design departments and some of the problems this entailed, as Sir Alfred Sims tried to get a grip on the several professional 'tribes'. One major project was the building of HM S/M *Dreadnought*, the Navy's first hunter–killer nuclear propelled submarine. Admiral Rickover USN, the father of all nuclear submarines once said that there were only two British admirals who had the brains to understand what he was doing; Mountbatten and Reid. True or untrue (and Rickover, a bit of a snob, was well aware that both had connections with Royalty) they were the only two men with whom he would meet and do business, and if the Navy was to catch up after the British government had so shortsightedly aborted the development of the RN's 'atomic boiler', Rickover's help was essential.

Reid, well aware of Rickover's sensitivities and of the problems facing Sir Alfred Sims, anticipated personality clashes, so he arranged that the *Dreadnought* should be brought to life by an almost autonomous executive team reporting personally to him as Controller, with Sims' ship department in a supportive and consultant role. Thus the Dreadnought Project Team (DPT) came into being, headed by a great eccentric but an even greater leader, some would say the greatest of all naval constructors of his era, Mr later Sir Rowland Baker RCNC. He had worked for Mountbatten in Combined Operations and designed many of the craft used in the Normandy

Launch of the Navy's first nuclear propelled hunter-killer submarine, HM S/M Dreadnought (photograph courtesy Vickers).

invasion. As his deputy, Baker had Captain later Rear-Admiral W T C Ridley CB one of the early 'revolutionaries' who was responsible for *Dreadnought*'s nuclear propulsion system. Inevitably as Mountbatten and Reid had predicted, Baker and Rickover clashed, and much emollient was needed to keep the show on the road, but the Dreadnought Project Team won through. On Trafalgar Day 1960, precisely on time and after months of hectic meetings in Reid's office between Rickover, Baker, Ridley, Jim (later Sir Denning) Pearson the great engineer and chairman of Rolls-Royce the main nuclear machinery contractors responsible for fitting the US machinery into the submarine, Sir Charles Dunphie and Leonard (later Sir Leonard) Redshaw, respectively chairman and general manager of Vickers the shipbuilders, HM S/M *Dreadnought* was ready to take the water. She was launched at Barrow in Furness by the Queen, in the presence of a mighty throng and a faintly smiling Admiral Rickover, triumphantly produced by me, his aide for the day, at the right moment and in his uniform, sword and all, to receive the Royal thanks for his great and 'happy' cooperation. Unlike Admiral Levering Smith USN, father of the Polaris missile, Rickover would never accept the honorary knighthood offered him as a token of British appreciation for all his help.

The dilemma of who was to be ultimately responsible to the Board for the fleet's mobility, with the disappearance of the Engineer in Chief of the Fleet, was mentioned in the last chapter. There was no doubt in Reid's mind, despite Sir Alfred Sims' resolute rejection of the idea, that the Director of Marine Engineering (DME), Sims' sub-ordinate in the ship department, was the man on whom the responsibility for the mobility of the fleet should rest, but Reid, always intensely loyal to his subordinates, was still reluctant to overrule Sims' objections to this course.

The right moment to do so came when HMS *Ark Royal* was temporarily delayed by engine trouble from leaving Singapore on a politically important mission. If Reid had a failing it was a suspicion of politicians; he was apt to be defensive and not at his best in his dealings with them. Just before the *Ark Royal* problem surfaced Reid had been sent for by Lord Carrington, the First Lord, because of trouble with the development of a torpedo. Observing on Car-rington's desk a file with a heading in large letters by a young assistant secretary (now a famous permanent secretary in the Welsh Office) which read, 'FAILURE OF THE....TORPEDO', Reid pro-duced a classic, 'First Lord, I'm sorry your young man has reported this as a failure. It isn't that it has *failed*—it's just that it doesn't do what's expected of it!'

Reid was thus in no mood to be harried when, on returning to his office and having been told that *Ark Royal* had now sailed, he re-ceived a personal call from an angry prime minister Macmillan, demanding an explanation for the fact that *Ark Royal* was still in Sin-gapore. The Prime Minister was not in Reid's good books. He had removed from the Board of Admiralty (in the person of Admiral Reid, the Controller) the sponsorship of the shipbuilding industry which had carried the Nation through two world wars. To put it at its most charitable, Reid's reply on the subject of HMS *Ark Royal* was as courteous as always but notably brisk; and the Prime Minister hung up on him. As far as the fleet's mobility was concerned, this was the straw that broke the camel's back. Despite Sims' objections, the DME was made directly responsible to the Board for those duties in relation to the running fleet, once exercised by the Engineer in Chief of the Fleet. Later the DME became chairman of the marine engineering advisory committee (MEAC), which brought together the senior engineering officers in the fleet, from the working up team at Portland (where all ships go to make them fully battleworthy before joining the fleet), and those responsible for the entry and training of engineers, as well as a representative of the appointing authority. So the three lines of responsibility, first for materiel design responsibility and serviceability at sea, second for entry and training of technical ratings, and third for reports on competence of engineering officers, previously brought together in the post of the Engineer in Chief, were revived under the chairmanship of the DME; and somehow Sims was mollified.

A year or so before Reid was due to end his five years in the Controllership it became known that his likely successor would be Rear-Admiral Michael Le Fanu. In the course of a remarkable career as a gunnery officer Le Fanu who, like Reid, possessed a first class brain, had been liaison officer with the US Pacific fleet, naval assistant to a previous Controller and also to a First Sea Lord, AF Lord Fraser of North Cape. Currently he was recovering after a hard grind as Director-General (weapons) where he had suffered a slight heart attack. Reid, like the majority of his Board colleagues (except Lord Mountbatten) had always viewed with distaste the idea of the Navy being ordered to handle the national deterrent, although unlike them, he believed that for strategic reasons the Navy would one day be handed that reponsibility. If this happened, he guessed, there would be an expensive and panicky start to the detriment of resources available for the rest of his beloved fleet. He therefore provided Le Fanu with all the lessons learned from the Dreadnought project team (DPT) and bade him, during his sick leave, create a paper organisation, quite separate from the ship department (whose bureaucracy he had come to distrust), dedicated to building five Polaris submarines in the minimum time and with impeccable cost control. When Le Fanu's scheme arrived in Reid's office there was considerable anxiety as his writing was appalling. Eventually it was deciphered, transcribed into Admiralty jargon, its comprehensive brilliance revealed, circulated to the Board for agreement and filed away in case the need for it should ever arise.

Towards the end of Reid's time it was apparent that the naive hopes held by some naval officers, first that Mountbatten's tenure as Chief of Defence Staff would see the amalgamation of Coastal Command with the Fleet Air Arm or that the RAF should merge with the Navy or, as was also put forward that it should be disbanded altogether and split between the Army and the Navy, were all political non-starters. At the same time the hull life of Britain's existing carriers was such that the preliminary designs of a new strike carrier fleet were now starting to move onto the ship department's drawing boards as the ideas of an enthusiastic naval staff (headed by an airman First Sea Lord and an enthusiastic CDS) evolved.

In those days before the accelerating cost inflation of burgeoning and newly invented military hardware was fully comprehended, there was in general use a rather simplistic formula, deriving early cost estimates from probable ship displacement But even the skills of first Mr Lawrence, and then Mr Rydill, both amongst the foremost naval architects of the day, could not nearly meet all the staff requirements, even with a displacement of 50,000 tons. Using the out of date formula, this displacement still gave a cost estimate which, large as it was, Reid, with five years experience of ship costing, believed to be far too low, as did the Treasury who opposed the whole project. As opposition hardened so the naval staff began to dig in their toes. Reid was schizophrenic. All his Pacific experience taught him that for the Navy to possess its own organic airpower was an essential part of maritime war. Then his equally brilliant elder brother, Sir Edward Reid, chairman of Barings the merchant bankers, with a wide knowledge of the country's economic health, predicted national economic decline. For this reason, Sir Edward told his younger brother, as he saw it, the defence vote, from which the Navy hitherto had done so well, would never find room even for one carrier at the cost Peter Reid quoted, let alone the accelerating inflation adjusted cost of the five needed to keep three carriers operational, which was the stated requirement.

Reid felt he must offer his Board colleagues a compromise. So he told me, already on record in my evidence to the Mansergh committee as opposing giant carriers, to research the newly developing P 1127 vertical take off and landing (VTOL) aircraft and to discuss with the aircraft manufacturers the idea of simultaneously designing a more modest aircraft carrier and a VTOL aircraft to match. In a few weeks matters had progressed to the point where a meeting was essential and Reid convened a seminar with the naval staff, the ship designers and the aircraft designers and manufacturers, including Sir George Edwards then chairman of the British Aircraft Corporation and Sir Sydney Camm of Hawkers, the designer of the P 1127.

The meeting got off to an hilarious start as Bill Bedford, the P 1127 test pilot, arrived on crutches. This, he hastily explained, was due to a skiing accident, not the P 1127. From then on the discussion went steadily down hill. Obsessed with the heavy strike carrier concept of the US navy and of fleet protection as a secondary role, the naval staff believed that only the latest supersonic aircraft met the requirement. To keep three carriers at sea five would be needed, so five there must be; end of argument. Sir Alfred Sims was stuck with his costing, now generally accepted as an absolute ceiling, derived far too optimistically (and therefore too low) from a hull of 50,000 tons. A displacement which to Reid, aware of the American carrier programme (the naval staff's dream world), seemed to mean cramming a quart into a pint pot, with all the operational ills that such an attempt would entail. Impasse. To break it Reid asked Sir Sydney Camm to come back in six weeks with a carrier design suitable for the developed P 1127! At the same time, he asked Sir Alfred Sims to bring a legend and sketch design of what he conceived to be the answer to the naval staff's requirements within what he regarded as the bogus cost ceiling derived from a 50,000 ton displacement. The next meeting was worse. Sims submitted a design estimated, unbelievably, to take from seven to ten years to build the first of class from keel laying to acceptance. To make matters worse, Reid had found out that the steam propulsion system needed, if it was to be compressed into the size of hull, and approach the mobility, in terms of range and speed, demanded by the Naval staff, and have the boiler power for steam catapults (four demanded by the Naval staff but only two possible within a 50 000 ton hull) and ship services, was far more advanced than anything yet contemplated, even by the revolutionaries, as feasible in a warship. The electrics would be equally difficult.

Finally Sir Sydney Camm was permitted to offer his solution, a well thought out conceptual design for a gas turbine driven carrier, much smaller than that demanded by the Naval staff, but designed to accomodate possibly 12 developed P 1127 VTOL aircraft for which, at that time, even if developed into all that he foresaw, the Naval staff had no use. Camm's idea was almost identical to today's

Sir Sidney Camm, designer of the P 1127,
later the Harrier (photograph courtesy
British Aerospace).

Invincible class, with two exceptions. Camm proposed a common
fuel for the ship and aircraft, still not technically possible. Also there
was no ski slope at the end of the flight deck which would assist the
aircraft to take off with a larger fuel or armament load (thought of
later by a young (E) officer when *Invincible* was building).

However there was a strong feeling throughout the Navy that the
fleet must never again be permitted to do battle without its own organic airpower supplied by supersonic aircraft of the types operated
by the US Navy. Sadly, Reid was in a minority amongst his colleagues on the Board and saw that the time was not yet ripe for the
momentous change to VTOL aircraft that Camm proposed and Reid
had come to envisage. With his own tenure of office about to expire
in a few weeks, the project was filed, though not forgotten.

Although the training of technical ratings was the Second Sea
Lord's business, Reid, with the former's agreement, and with his
own awareness of how the Navy was moving into the future, took a
deep interest in HMS *Sultan* the propulsion ratings' training school
at Gosport, where Captain later Rear-Admiral Hugh Tracy, CB,
DSC, (one of the early 'revolutionaries'), was building up the technical training, as he had built up Manadon's professional training.
Reid, a supporter of the General List (Mansergh concept) sought and
obtained Board approval for Tracy to be chairman of a board of en-

quiry (a post hitherto exclusively reserved for executive officers) into a massive machinery failure in the newly refitted HMS *Lion*. The Board of Admiralty were delighted with the definitive and trenchant answers that Tracy produced. This was another small but significant milestone on the way to the rising influence of technology in the Navy.

It fell to me a decade later, to read the lesson at Admiral Sir Peter Reid's memorial service at St Martin in the Fields and to write his obituary in *The Times*. Like so many of his predecessors, Reid died early. In the battle for the Falklands a further ten years on, the fleet took heavy casualties because money had not been found, as Reid would have found it, to provide over the horizon radar. Most of the surface fleet, (as well as three nuclear powered Hunter–Killer submarines and one conventional diesel submarine), at last possessing such mobility that it could maintain itself at sea for 160 days, 8000 miles from base, firing its guns continually on the enemy and with a combat air patrol (CAP) of Harriers (ex P 1127) overhead from an all gas turbine carrier, had either been built, designed or conceived during Admiral Sir Peter Reid's historic Controllership.

Vice Admiral Sir Michael Le Fanu GCB, DSC
Third Sea Lord and Controller 1961–1965

Among the galaxy of talent on Fraser's Staff (in HMS Duke of York *in 1943) was the then Lieutenant-Commander Michael Le Fanu, destined in 1961 to become the Navy's youngest Controller in seventy years, to mastermind the plans for Britain's Polaris fleet and, like Fraser, to rise to First Sea Lord and Admiral of the Fleet.*

Fraser of North Cape
Richard Humble

THE NAVAL ASSISTANT

If he writes tactfully—he's verbose.
If he drafts a report, he's wrong—if he doesn't there's nothing to work on:
If he advises, he's butting in—if he doesn't he's slack.
If he asks for a decision he's cheeky—if he doesn't he's incompetent.
If a meeting is a success, its the committee—if it's a failure, its the NA.
If he asks for instructions, he's no initiative—if he doesn't
he's swollen headed.
Ashes to ashes—dust to dust—if others won't do it, THE NA MUST.

Words by Captain Michael Le Fanu
NA to Controller and later to First Sea Lord

Admiral Sir Michael Le Fanu was as different from Admiral Reid as chalk from cheese. The latter had been brought up in the shadow of Royalty, was the godson of a King and often the guest of the Queen in the Royal Yacht *Britannia*. Mike Le Fanu held that he had been brought up as a barefoot boy in County Cork where his father, unjustly retired as a captain from the Navy on an inadequate pension, had chosen to settle.

Their attitudes were best revealed in their choice of transport. Reid, when travelling north (where his home had always been) to the shipyards went by LNER (never on any account LMS) sleeper, most of whose attendants he seemed to know by name. Le Fanu, because he always tried to get home to his brave wife crippled by polio and confined to a wheelchair, always took to the air. Reid abhorred any symptom of 'playing to the gallery', and loathed and avoided the media. Le Fanu played to the gallery as a deliberate attempt to reduce the aura of pomposity that he felt some in the service's hierarchy were too apt to assume, rather than to promote his own image. Inevitably however, the first could not proceed without something of the second; and his enemies and those jealous of his quick rise denigrated his 'play acting', as they called it. It was one of the more hazardous duties of the author, his naval assistant, sometimes and usually unsuccessfully, to restrain the Controller's more dramatic gambits.

It may have been the leukaemia from which Le Fanu so tragically died soon after he was appointed Chief of Defence Staff that was beginning to affect him, but he was a man of moods who overworked a not very strong frame and was, as a result, occasionally overcome by what Churchill would have described as his 'black dog'. In truth Le Fanu, a much younger man than Reid or his Board colleagues, a man of deep humility, was sometimes a little unsure of himself and lacked Reid's gravitas. Once he had made up his mind, however, he would never bend. Above all Le Fanu was a good and loyal companion with a vast in-built fund of human kindness, which he often took great pains to conceal.

Professionally Le Fanu, like the rest of the Board, was a convinced big carrier man and Reid's dalliance with the aircraft industry was at once put on the shelf. When my time came to go to the Imperial Defence College my relief was an outstanding naval pilot, not an engineer, but also a dedicated big carrier man.

As Director-General(weapons) Le Fanu had sensed a lack of leadership in the ship department under Sir Alfred Sims but, like most people, had a love/hate relationship with Sims and a very clear understanding of the appalling problems that he so staunchly faced. It had always been assumed that another member of the Royal Corps of Naval Constructors would relieve Sims in due course, but so strongly did Le Fanu feel that the ship department would need the best leader the Navy could find regardless of specialisation or professional discipline, that one of his earliest actions as Controller was to win the First Lord's approval, against much contrary pressure, for the post of Director-General (ships), in the future, to always be considered 'ad hominem', as the Nihill committee had rather limply suggested.

Le Fanu was an exponent of mobility and, as with Reid, the 'revolutionaries' at Bath had a friend. It was at Le Fanu's suggestion that Captain R G Raper, one of the original engineering 'revolutionaries' of twenty years before, was earmarked as a future Director of Marine Engineering. Later, as Vice Admiral Sir George Raper, he succeeded Sir Alfred Sims as Director-General (ships).

Meanwhile as Controller Le Fanu was not above politicking, something Reid would never have tolerated, so I was told to draft a letter to *The Times* criticising the money currently being spent on Concorde and comparing it with the pittance allocated to British shipyards. This draft was sent in final form to the 14 chairmen of the warship group of shipbuilders and only one, Vickers, declined to sign it: understandably enough as the firm was involved with the Concorde project. The letter's publication brought no political response.

Enthused by a presentation of their design for a nuclear engined fleet support tanker at the Yarrow-Admiralty Research Department (YARD) in Glasgow, Le Fanu tentatively suggested to the Board that the Navy should cut its teeth with a nuclear tanker before considering nuclear propulsion for surface warships. The Board, weighed down with the carrier controversy, were less than encouraging.

A year after Le Fanu had become Third Sea Lord and Controller, besides carrying on Reid's work of building an up to date and well weaponed Navy and making plans to send the first all gas turbined major warship to sea, he found himself bringing forward the plans that Reid's foresight had asked him to write for building a fleet of Polaris nuclear missile submarines. The organisation Le Fanu had originally proposed, which largely eliminated red tape, was once more quickly examined by the Board and approved for action. Vice Admiral Sir Hugh Mackenzie KCB, DSO*, DSC, a famous wartime submarine ace and ex-flag officer, submarines, was nominated as chief Polaris executive, with Sir Rowland Baker, RCNC (largely responsible for HMS *Dreadnought*) as his technical director and one of the great Admiralty civil servants, Mr Peter Nailor (now Professor Peter Nailor) as finance director, to hold the purse strings. A team of constructors under Mr Sidney Palmer RCNC, CB, (later Head of the Royal Corps of Naval Constructors), propulsion engineers under

Captain Dorian Dymoke (later Rear-Admiral Dymoke CB), and weapon engineers under Captain Charles Shepherd (later Rear-Admiral Shepherd CB, CBE) together with logistics experts and civil servants provided one of the most highly professional and skilled managerial teams the country has known. In conjunction with Vickers the builders, Rolls-Royce the machinery contractors and the UK Polaris liaison team in the US, the result is still regarded as uniquely successful, achieving, as it did, completion of the whole vast Polaris programme precisely on time and well within the original cost estimate.

Chapter 16
Less Weight and Larger Power: Towards Improved Mobility 1964–1967

> *We're creeping on with each new rig—*
> *less weight and larger power*
>
> *McAndrew's Hymn*
> Rudyard Kipling

Kipling understood engineering, and although McAndrew's Hymn has type-cast all engineers as being rather rough Scots, it was such men, English, Welsh and Irish as well as Scots, the 'revolutionaries' of their day, who pressed forward the industrial revolution on sea and land. In the Royal Navy, from 1942 onwards, less weight and larger power was the constant aim, whether it was expressed in terms of steam, diesel, gas turbine or nuclear propulsion.

By the time Vice Admiral Sir Horace Law relieved Vice Admiral Sir Michael Le Fanu as Controller in 1965, the 1942 seeds sown by the (E) 'revolutionaries' had taken root, and all ships building and recently commissioned were of increasingly superior mobility. HM S/M *Dreadnought*, Britain's first nuclear submarine was at sea and her all British hunter-killer successors were on the slips, as were the four Polaris missile nuclear propelled submarines.

Prima facie to Admiral Law, like his predecessor a gunnery specialist, there must have been much that seemed satisfactory, not least in the advancing quality of weapons, but in several areas of his responsibility there were great worries, some of which have already been mentioned or hinted at; and many of which his predecessors had initiated actions designed to cure. For various reasons some of the progress made in recent years was at risk.

Although the problem which bedevilled the Admiralty when the results of the Mansergh (officer structure) and the Nihill (rationalisation of design departments) committees clashed, militating against keeping the fleet at a peak of mobility, this difficulty had been solved

177

by Admiral Reid in 1961. By 1964, four separate but significant grounds for further worry had emerged. First, during the interregnum when the responsibility for keeping the (largely new) fleet serviceable was blurred, and before the ship maintenance authority (SMA) was fully staffed and organised, the frigates, particularly, had been kept operating longer than they should have and had fallen badly behind in their maintenance schedules. Too many defects had piled up. Second, as this was happening, the political need for operational warships increased well beyond the serviceability for which they had been designed. For these two reasons unserviceability became uncomfortably common. Third, the lack of sufficient prototype development running for the new steam propulsion units began to show up in component failures, some of these due to an initially wrong estimation of mean time between failure (MTBF), the majority due to too long running without component replacement. Lastly, there had been an underestimation of the spare gear stocks deriving from the same lack of prototype running data, a lower stated requirement for serviceability than, in practice, was necessary to meet the political requirements demanded of an already overstretched Navy in peacetime, and last the inevitable lack of money invested in readily available spare gear and stores.

Rear-Admiral Tracy, lately Captain of HMS *Sultan*, was now the Director of Marine Engineering, and, as his deputy, I was responsible to him for ship machinery design and the running fleet, (the other deputy being responsible for research and development). By 1964–65, swift and rather dramatic action was needed to rectify a rapidly deteriorating ship serviceability situation despite the fact that a much closer liaison between the marine engineering directorate and the operations division of the naval staff was introducing some realism into the operational periods between ship maintenance intervals. So Operation MOBUS (mobility is our business) was launched by Admiralty Fleet Order. Some £1/2M was allocated to Tracy, together with a no-nonsense commander (Commander later Rear-Admiral P B Hogg CB) with delegated authority to order, purchase and distribute spare machinery items, where their lack was interfering with serviceability. Quite quickly, thanks mainly to Hogg and the quick reactions of the manufacturers, the situation improved and a united front was created between the operators, who were trying to meet the constant political demands for ships to go here there and everywhere, and the marine engineers responsible for keeping the ships workable. Much weaponry was similarly afflicted by constant unserviceability, but in a cold, or non-shooting, war it was mobility that was called for, and the need for operational weaponry, which might not in fact have been fully met, was less apparent. Those responsible saw the warning signs, and similar steps to rectify weapon problems were put in hand.

The practical problems involved in designing a strike carrier and giving it the fighting power the naval staff wished, within a price restricted hull displacement, the latter a little over half what was really required, have already been mentioned. Speed and endurance were going to be far less than that called for; only two catapults, not the four envisaged could be provided and (in the words of D K Brown RCNC in his book, *A Century of Naval Construction*) CVA-01 was to be a 'furniture van', with a novel light structure and no armour, not even over the magazines. It was estimated that the first of class would take ten years to build and put into commission; and this at a time of galloping price inflation.

The practical problems were accentuated by the psychological ones. The Board of Admiralty had determined on five big carriers; the Treasury was adamantly opposed. The RAF were desperately disappointed at their forthcoming loss of the national nuclear deterrent, a responsibility they had trained for and carried out resolutely for so long. Their new TSR2 advanced aircraft was now in the prototype trials stage. Trade protection (the Navy's business as the Navy saw it) could become the responsibility of the RAF without any need for expensive carriers (as the RAF's always very effective public relations saw it) by adopting the RAF's suddenly conceived 'island strategy', the alleged ability to deploy airpower in defence of the trade routes from British bases around the world. Apart from making the same logistic mistake as Montgomery and Tedder had made at the RUSI in 1954 over the massive fuel supplies needed by aircraft—which would have to come by sea—such a strategy, though swallowed by many naive politicians and some of the media, was politically and geographically bogus. All these pressures acted on the team of carrier designers at Bath, who well knew that they themselves were too thin on the ground, that there was much planned equipment for the carrier as yet quite undeveloped, and that the final true cost would be prohibitive. They turned their talents to designing a tie, which they all came to wear, of a gold aircraft carrier on a blue background with a big red axe hanging over it.

It all ended in a terrible fiasco. The Board, including the Controller, had committed themselves to a cost given by the Director-General (ships) Sir Alfred Sims, with hindsight derived from a formula entirely irrelevant and outdated to the general pattern of naval hardware design in the 1960s. Sims, despite the views of his brilliant but loyal subordinates, refused to go to the Board and say, 'on a more detailed examination and because of price inflation of naval equipment the warfighting capability you are asking me to provide within the original estimate and hull size is no longer possible'.

Two tragedies ensued. With the advent of Mr Healey, a tough, perceptive, socialist Secretary of State, a political decision was made to cancel the carrier and the TSR2 projects. The Board of Admiralty considered resignation. On realising that resignation meant the forfeiture of all pension rights, the First Sea Lord, Admiral Sir David Luce GCB, DSO*, OBE, never himself such an enthusiastic proponent of the carrier fleet as his colleagues, but largely out of loyalty to them, asked to retire. Thus he sacrificed promotion to Admiral of the Fleet and the Navy lost the first submarine specialist to hold the post at the very moment when his expertise was needed after half a century of British neglect of the submarine. Christopher Mayhew, a loyal First Lord, also destroyed a promising political career by resigning on the fundamentally sound grounds that commitments had to be cut before resources. A few years later, when Britain abandoned any naval presence East of Suez, Mayhew's advice was taken.

Throughout the twenty years after the carrier/island strategy drama, there was much prevarication and talk by the Navy (still terrified of the impact of RAF public relations on gullible politicians and the media), of 'through deck cruisers' and helicopter carriers. Thanks largely to Admiral Reid's prescience, and Sir Sydney Camm's imaginative aircraft (and carrier) design, when the need arose in the Falklands, the Navy had the *Invincibles* and the Harriers to go with them.

In these days when every child from the age of four knows how to work a computer, it is astonishing to realise with what suspicion in the 1960s Sir Alfred Sims and others regarded these new fangled contraptions. It was Admiral Tracy, who first introduced computers to the marine engineering directorate. Tracy had some major problems facing him, and his management expertise, as he had shown in previous appointments, was ahead of many others in the ship department and on a par with Sir Rowland Baker in the Polaris team and Mr Fitzer the deputy director of electrical engineering. The first move Tracy made was to carry out a study of precisely how each man and woman in all the sections of the marine engineering directorate spent their working hours. From that study a more effectively directed and cost efficient management of DME's directorate evolved. Within a few years in the rest of the ship department, computer aided ship design took the place of the laboriously written workbooks, the bane of young constructors, but the sacred cows of the constructive hierarchy. It was another 'revolution'.

Reference was made in chapter 15 to Admiral Le Fanu's failed attempt to interest the Admiralty Board in surface nuclear propulsion. Despite this, the Yarrow-Admiralty Research Department in Glasgow, at their own expense, had produced a seemingly viable design for a nuclear propelled tanker, and I had written a series of articles on naval strategy in the *Journal of the Royal United Services Institute* ('The one open highway', 'World population and British strategy', 'Peace is our profession', 'All oceans lead to England' and others) outlining the need for the constant presence of a small British task force supported by nuclear tankers and replenishment ships in the Aden/Singapore/Perth/Capetown ocean area. This idea was cribbed from General Sir John Hackett's Constabulary Concept for the armed forces suggested by his Lees-Knowles lectures and Lord Mountbatten's belief, although he advocated large carriers and I did not, of a naval peacekeeping force in the Indian Ocean/Arabian Sea. As my views, not for the first time, were disregarded by the Navy, though not by students at the Army Staff College, for whom I was told my Articles were compulsory reading, and senior officers in the Pentagon, one of whom made his way to Bath to cross-examine me, I turned to the Press. It was before the days when Mr Healey had forbidden officers of the services to talk to the media and so, in various hostelries in Bath and London, I urged Nowell Hall of the *Daily Telegraph*, David Divine of the *Sunday Times*, Chapman Pincher of the *Daily Express* and others to take up the cudgels not only on behalf of nuclear propulsion for warships, but also those other two essential elements of a maritime nation, the wholly neglected merchant navy and fishing fleets. Alas, despite their efforts, though they caused a flutter in the Admiralty dovecot, it was all to no avail; although David Divine's books, *The Blunted Sword* and *The Broken Wing* probably owed something to the cheerful exchanges encouraged by a number of notably liquid lunches.

There were two more marine engineering problems to be solved in 1966. Although the 'through deck cruiser'/helicopter carrier was still only in the very conceptual stage, Sir Sydney Camm's idea of a common fuel for aircraft and ships' gas turbines had to be explored, as also had a common fuel for the steam/gas turbine fleet, if gas turbines were to become the standard propulsion unit as we in the marine engineering directorate advocated. Such a change-over of main propulsion units would take twenty years or more during which the fleet would have steam turbine and gas turbine driven ships. Either there would have to be a supply of one fuel for gas turbines and and another for boilers, a hopeless logistic task, or a fuel which could be burnt satisfactorily and safely in both would have to be agreed with the industry and an acceptable specification drawn up. Luckily (*chapter 10*) I had been secretary to the Admiralty Oil Quality Committee twenty years before and, as a Fellow of the Institute of Petroleum, was in touch with some of the industry's major figures including Dr Drinkwater from the National Gas Turbine Establishment, to whom the Navy was already indebted for much help in the past. As has always been the case with the oil companies, they rallied round and with the assistance of the Admiralty Fuel Experimental Station, and the new Admiralty Oil Laboratory set up as a result of the Geddes committee, a fuel specification suitable both for boilers and gas turbines was established, tested and finally approved. However, the volatility of the fuel necessary for aircraft engines was judged to be still too dangerous to stow in ordinary ships' fuel tanks, requiring instead specially designed stowage. Sir Sydney Camm's idea of a common fuel for carrier propulsion gas turbines and aircraft was deemed impracticable. I believe it still is.

Perhaps the most significant move towards improved mobility was taken towards the end of Admiral Tracy's period in office. Over a period of nearly twenty-five years under Commanders Hall, Baker, Tracy, Trewby, Dymoke, Flower *et al*, the Royal Navy had been developing and 'marinising' (making fit for sea service) gas turbines of increasing sophistication and reliability. But no major war vessel had yet been fitted with gas turbines as the sole source of propulsive power. The change from steam to gas turbines had its pros and cons and these needed to be set out.

As the large numbers of brawny stokers needed for coal fired boilers gave way to the rather smaller numbers of stokers, not necessarily so physically robust, needed for oil fired boilers, so with gas turbines there could be a considerable reduction in the number of operators compared to those needed for oil fired boilers, although those left would need a rather higher intelligence quotient. Thus accomodation space would be saved but living conditions would need improving, and training also. The changeover from one form of propulsion to another, as new ships replaced old, would take another twenty-five years, during which men would sometimes serve in a steam ship and sometimes in a gas turbine ship, so there were quite difficult personnel problems to be recognised and surmounted.

In the materiel field the great advantage would be that gas turbines adapted from aircraft engines would have been subjected to many thousands of hours of test-bed running, as against the difficulty with steam propulsion units that it was never economic to build a ship's whole machinery set ashore, boiler and all and a brake to absorb the energy, and then subject it to prolonged shore running to remove any 'bugs' or design faults before fitting in a ship. Against this, steam sets once proved at sea could run for years with regular maintenance. Gas turbine machinery, like aircraft engines, required replacement after a set number of hours. In aircraft the engine is normally hung on the wing, or in other ways was comparatively easily replaceable. In ships the difficulties were formidable. As already mentioned, a gas turbine required a vast volume of air and the air downtakes had to be designed so that this flow of air was constant, otherwise engine surging occured, possibly with catastrophic results. The air downtake was also the obvious route for an engine change and the shaping of the two requirements had to be made compatible. In addition such large holes from the upper deck down to the bowels of the ship had to be designed to cause minimum danger should the ship be damaged in action and flooding occur. Another problem with which naval constructors had to cope was that of stability. Steam machinery and boilers were heavy and brought down the ship's centre of gravity so that topweight in the shape of heavy radar aerials high up, could, to some extent, be accomodated. Gas turbines were lighter so the topweight and stability problems, especially in cases of action damage, could prove fatal if careful design had not provided for such a contingency.

Operationally, gas turbines meant that the ship could get underway in an emergency in minutes and the ship could literally be driven from the bridge. With a steam plant, unless steam had been

HMS Exmouth, *the first major warship to be propelled solely by gas turbine (photograph courtesy Lt Comdr Maber).*

raised and a watch was on duty in the boiler and engine rooms, it would be a matter of two to three hours or more depending on 'the notice for steam', before the ship was ready to move.

Although by 1966 the individual members of the Board of Admiralty had had many years of steady indoctrination by the 'revolutionaries', as well as by Admirals Reid and Le Fanu, into the merits of gas turbine propulsion, and was led by one of the great post-war First Sea Lords, a much decorated destroyer officer Admiral Sir Varyl Begg, it was still true that, except in coastal forces, there was as yet no major warship propelled *solely* by gas turbines. As Britain was leading the world there was no experience outside Britain on which to call. Admiral Begg was picking up the pieces after the carrier disaster and to him must go the credit of restoring the Navy's morale and at the same time making the Navy's peace with the Secretary of State; but he knew, and we knew, that any further design catastrophe would harm the Navy irreparably. So Tracy, aware that Sims was not altogether 'sold' on gas turbines largely because of the admittedly difficult constructive problems to do with air intakes and stability, and that the Board, still lacking any engineers, would rely greatly on Sims' advice for such a major policy change, wisely proposed that a Blackwood class steamship, HMS *Exmouth*, should have a gas turbine propulsion set of machinery substituted for its existing steam set and thus provide a floating test bed.

In due course, thanks to a brilliant explanatory paper for the Board, originally drafted by Commander later Rear-Admiral E J W Flower CB, the success of *Exmouth* and the advocacy of Rear-Admiral (soon to be Vice Admiral) Sir George Raper, first as Tracy's successor and then as Sims', the Board accepted the change *in toto* and thereby, over the ensuing decade and a half, restored to much of the fleet, the best mobility achievable for surface ships short of nuclear propulsion, which, alas, still eludes the Royal Navy.

Chapter 17
Management of Warship Design

Our challenge is to overcome an atmosphere in which all sense of reverence for the unique and therefore the capacity for real innovation stands in danger of being lost.

The Necessity for Choice
Henry Kissinger 1961

By 1967, after twenty five years of engineering revolution to which so many had contributed, the fuse was burning that, fifteen years later, was to give the fleet the mobility it needed in the Falklands. The very demons of technology unearthed in the new and complex types of propulsion machinery and weapon systems, by their cost, created new and unpredictable inflationary pressures, and combined to make the effective management of warship design more difficult than ever before.

Much as the Nihill committee had done to improve the combined efforts of the different engineering disciplines in the departments concerned, a total warship design concept with improved cost estimation had still not been achieved. Geography, in part, was to blame. The ship department was on one hill, the weapon and dockyard departments on another, on the opposite sides of a busy city. Face to face discussion was always difficult.

Changes in strategic thinking and in politicians (the latter often without experience of war and technically illiterate); the national economic climate; the gleams in the eyes of scientists; intelligence input as to the threat; such considerations were only the beginning of the puzzle. Fuel load (range) versus speed versus armament versus sea keeping qualities were only material starting points from which could stem an almost infinite number of variables. There was also the human side. Somewhere in this maze, men (and now women) of different abilities and qualifications, all aspiring to higher living standards and all subject to a somewhat unnatural discipline measured against an increasingly homogenised society, had somehow to be reasonably accomodated in an artificial division, derived partly from tradition and partly from expediency. Above all a warship had to float for as long as possible despite what the enemy could do to it; it had to move for as far and as long as possible, and fight whenever and wherever in the world that was needed.

Sir Michael Cary, the Permanent Secretary, persuaded Admiral Le Fanu to go outside the Navy and bring in Messrs Urwick Orr, the management consultants, for a fresh view of the warship design management problem. Because I had seen the other side of the coin from the office of the Controller, I was nominated to be their liaison officer and to try to smooth their path in the restrained welcome to which all such consultants are accustomed, while still retaining my duties as deputy director of marine engineering (DDME).

The Royal Corps of Naval Constructors (RCNC) was primarily a highly qualified group of naval architects specialising in warship design and repair. In this role they rightly saw themselves as the co-ordinators, having to impose on the other disciplines all the infuriating restrictions dictated by the laws of physics, hull design, stability, living space and an environmental factor ranging from the Arctic and the Antarctic to the equator. Constructors were the umpires between the competing claims of the naval staff, who wanted perfection in all things, and the mechanical, electrical, electronic and chemical engineers who sought, sometimes rather uncompromisingly, to give of their best.

A history of the training and achievements of the RCNC is told well in *A Century of Naval Construction* by D K Brown (Conway). Briefly, personnel of the RCNC were selected from amongst the cleverest of dockyard (mainly shipwright) apprentices who were then further educated at the Royal Naval College (RNC), Greenwich and, later at the Royal Naval Engineering College (RNEC), Manadon, and University college, London (UCL), to a very high graduate and post graduate standard. To support them in Bath they had a strong band of constructive draughtsmen. When at sea the constructors wore uniform with a grey shipwright stripe between the gold. In the background there was a powerful Royal Corps Association 'pay and conditions' negotiating body, to which all constructors belonged.

Many of the civilian electrical engineers came from the same background as the constructors and trained in their particular discipline at the same establishments. Others had electrical engineering degrees from university.

The full story of the birth, education and training of the naval mechanical/marine engineer officer corps has been told by Commander Geoffrey Penn in his two books, *Up Funnel, Down Screw* (Hollis and Carter) and *HMS* Thunderer, (Kenneth Mason). To recapitulate briefly, their role was, with practical sea experience, to be able to converse on equal professional terms with scientists and skilled engineers in industry and interpret to them the particular future engineering needs of the Navy as set out by the naval staff, at the same time bringing to the notice of the latter those new advances in technology likely to enhance the fighting charateristics of warships.

By the 1960s certain facts were becoming plain. The size and shape of the fleet was restricting the number of seagoing billets in which junior naval graduate engineers could absorb the essential experience permitting them at a later stage, first to play this interpretive role between industry and the naval staff and also to give practical guidance based on their sea experience, to civilian machinery and weapon designers. Simultaneously and embarrassingly with this restriction on graduate (uniformed) engineers, the rapid advances and increasing complexity of technology created a need for even more graduate guidance of engineering design both in house and by the Admiralty departments to the related industries. Something had to give and so the civilian Royal Naval Engineering Service (RNES) was born.

Initially the RNES consisted of retired engineering officers recruited on a civilian basis, many with experience of war at sea. As they reached a second retirement age (from the RNES) civilian graduates without sea experience had to be recruited. Simultaneously, the new seagoing uniformed naval electrical branch, now beginning to have an impact both in the weapon field and the civilian directorate of electrical engineering, was encountering similar difficulties. There were not enough ships to give the uniformed graduate electrical engineers the practical seagoing knowledge they needed, so civilian electrical engineers (and, incidentally, exponents of the new professional discipline of production engineering (PE)), also joined the RNES. While such RNES officers were not sea experienced like the uniformed officers, some of the younger graduates were sent to sea or to the RN Engineering College. Thus, in one way or another, a fruiful 'rubbing off' process ensured that the unique difficulties to be faced in all aspects of warship design became better understood by the increasingly civilian element in the design departments.

My job was to introduce Urwick Orr to these different professional disciplines and tribal traditions. There were quasi-civilian graduate constructors (RCNC), uniformed (graduate) naval seagoing mechanical, nuclear and electrical engineers, civilian (graduate) mechanical, nuclear and electrical engineers (RNES), production engineers (RNES) and the old established Royal Naval Scientific Service (RNSS) besides non-graduate constructive, mechanical and electrical draughtemen of various grades and enormous experience. In addition there were a number of technical illustrators and civil servants dealing with general administration.

In his otherwise well researched book, Mr D K Brown rather plays down the problems facing the ship department, as well as the efforts of the Urwick Orr team and the subsequent Turner working party to improve matters. The management consultants were greatly impressed by the high quality Naval officers and civilian officials of the various tribes. They appreciated that the rivalry, common among most mixtures of professionals, was not unique to the Navy, although Urwick Orr were deeply impressed by the way that all sides in Bath were united in aiming to produce better and more war worthy ships, however much they sometimes differed over the means to do so. Urwick Orr were fortified in their view that basically all would be well if their recommendations were accepted, by the obvious efficiency and friendly sense of united purpose in the functionally managed Polaris team under Admiral Sir Hugh Mackenzie and Sir Rowland Baker RCNC; and also by their visit to the YARD in Glasgow, where a thriving inter-disciplinary management structure had always existed.

Sir Alfred Sims, the Director-General, could not bring himself to accept the functional management Urwick Orr proposed in place of the individual management pyramids of the different professional disciplines which had always existed, pre and post the Nihill committee reforms and which, despite much individual goodwill, too often lined up against each other.

At this stage Admiral Sir Horace Law entered the scene as Admiral Le Fanu's relief in the post of Third Sea Lord and Controller of the Navy. The former was a brave and decorated gunnery officer with much battle experience, later president of the officer's Christian Union and chairman of the Church Army Brigade. At first he had to tread warily, before gaining sufficient assurance either to back Sims or Urwick Orr, so Sir Michael Cary, the last Permanent Secretary (PUS) of the Admiralty, in an illustrious line stretching back to Pepys, took a hand. As an RNVR radar specialist at sea in the war he had an understanding of engineering, at that time all too rare amongst his civil service colleagues.

Cary kicked the ball into touch by setting up a working party to consider the Urwick Orr report. This consisted of the deputy directors of naval construction (DDNC), and electrical engineering (DDEE) and I represented the marine engineering directorate. Mr Fitzer the DDEE and a leader of great personal charm, was also vice chairman of the newly formed civilian RNES association now being seen by the RCNC Association as a rival. The chairman of the working party was Mr E A Turner, the senior administrative civil servant in Bath and an official of the highest calibre; the secretary was another brilliant civil servant who now adorns the Welsh office as its Permanent Secretary, Sir Richard Lloyd-Jones KCB.

Under such an able chairman, and with Mr Lloyd-Jones' Balliol inspired prose, the working party quickly identified the two main problems which they would have to tackle head-on. Their first aim was to emulate the Mansergh committee which gave birth to the General List of naval officers and so produce an 'all of one company' sentiment amongst the different professional tribes in Bath. The second was to establish, within the heart of the whole Bath organisation, a group or cell with the capability, by more accurate cost and manpower forecasting, of preventing the sort of disaster which the carrier controversy had inflicted on the Navy in general and on the credibility of the Board of Admiralty, in the eyes of the politicians, in particular.

The best way to an 'all of one company' attitude seemed to be that recommended by Urwick Orr. That was a balanced pattern of directors and deputy directors of different professional disciplines, under the Director-General, each responsible to him for a well defined element of the many aspects of warship design. There was plenty of superior talent in Bath and the working party, like Urwick Orr, saw no difficulty in creating a balance of functional directorates, as Sir Rowland Baker with his Polaris team and the YARD had already established.

The second problem, the working party believed, could be solved by the creation from within the ship department, of what they called a Forward Design and Resources Directorate. This would be a small but interdisciplinary, mainly graduate manned directorate. It would be charged to work closely with the naval staff, industry, the RNSS, with the weapons and dockyard departments and, most importantly, with that part of the Admiralty Secretariat dealing with the naval budget. Its task would be to produce for the Board a catalogue of warship designs accurately costed as far as possible, in terms of time, manpower and money, for the different mixes of machinery and weapons which might be practical options over the ensuing five years and also less accurate proposals for the more distant future.

Given the above, the majority of the working party believed that the Board and the Secretary of State would be more likely to receive a valid time and money and people costed project definition, for whatever type of warship might be envisaged by the Board, well before the taking of any irreversible decisions.

Unhappily the deputy director of naval construction (DDNC) on the Turner working party, Mr Perry, could not accept either solution and wrote a minority report condemning both proposals, the Forward Design and Resources Directorate particularly fiercely. Henceforth this was the main target for all who disagreed with the Urwick Orr/Turner proposals.

Quite quickly the situation became even more complicated. The comparatively new RNES association accepted the working party's views *in toto* but there was a split in the RCNC Association. The Director-General and the director of naval construction (DNC) and several of the constructor hierarchy firmly backed Mr Perry's minority report disagreeing with the Urwick Orr/Turner working party proposals, but the chairman of the RCNC Association (Mr Hancock) bravely came down in favour of the Turner majority, as did a number of the senior/middle rank constructors and (although their opinion was never formally invited) most of the junior constructors, some of whom had been (E) officers with me at Manadon and who put their views to me strongly. The production engineers, at the time just joining the RNES, backed the majority of the Turner working party, as did the Royal Naval Scientific Service (RNSS).

The chasm was a deep one and the Controller's position unenviable. Sir Alfred Sims and the director of naval construction (DNC), Mr Sherwin, united in opposition, were both men of total integrity whose outstanding contribution to warship design over the years was immeasurable. Mr Fitzer, deputy director of electrical engineering (DDEE), strongly in favour of the majority view, saw the weapon and sensor problems of the future more clearly than most. With my experience in the office of the Controller and of the carrier debacle, I was aware that for all the great work the ship department was performing it was, outside the nuclear submarine field, losing its credibility especially in its cost estimates; and Rear-Admiral Raper the new DME agreed. The need for more accurate early financial and manpower cost estimation was a feature of the warship design task constantly being pressed on Mr Turner in Bath by Sir Michael Cary the Permanent Secretary in London.

It became clear that the fundamental disagreement rested mainly, though not wholly, on the interpretation of the duties of the post of the Director-General, ships (DGS), as defined by Nihill in a rather woolly way, and as these duties were similarly interpreted by Sir Alfred Sims himself, the reigning Director-General. That Sims (DGS) was primus inter pares among the three Directors General of ships, weapons and dockyards was common ground, but Sims based his interpretation of his duties on the fact that he happened to be head (tribal chief) of the whole Royal Corps of Naval Constructors (RCNC) who were by tradition (and rightly) the coordinators of warship design. The opposite view was taken by the majority of the Turner working party. As they saw it the Director-General (ships),

Vice Admiral Sir George Raper, KBE
(photograph courtesy Lady Raper).

while certainly primus inter pares with the other two Directors-General, was in charge of a hull and power agency, just as the Director-General (weapons) was in charge of a weapon agency and the Director-General (dockyards and maintenance) a repair and refit agency.

Beyond leading a hull and power agency, the majority of the working party asserted that the Director-General (ships) possessed a coordinating authority stemming from the fact that Sims, regardless of the fact that he happened to be a naval constructor, was also by his office, de jure and de facto the Controller's *total ship* design and production *manager*, with a degree of authority second only to the Controller himself. That, the working party majority held, was why, as a Director-General he had the word *ships* after his title. Further, the word *total* comprised, besides pure ship design, a responsibility for the proper control of resources, essentially manpower and money, such as Admiral Mackenzie, the Chief Polaris Executive, ruthlessly exercised through his finance director Mr Peter Nailor, in the Polaris submarine project.

This comprehensive responsibility, the working party continued to proclaim, was why the ship department was the heart of the Controller's organisation, but a heart that could not beat properly so long as it lacked a control mechanism such as the Forward Design and Resources Directorate, which they recommended. The working party regarded the headship of the RCNC (tribal chief of the RCNC, as CNEO was tribal chief of naval engineers, and as Mr Tucker in the dockyard department was tribal chief of the RNES) as wholly irrelevant to the argument. Sir Alfred Sims, on the other hand, continued to hold strongly that it was his post as head of the Royal Corps that gave him infallible and almost papal authority over all other tribes in the warship design complex at Bath. None of these, particularly the uniformed officers and the RNES (or indeed many constructors) would accept such an arrangement, and although I could never divulge that I knew about it, the fact that Rear-Admiral Raper, a naval engineer, was to be the next, as yet unannounced, Director-General (ships) of course negated Sims' argument completely.

To try to find a way through this maze, as baffling to the reader as it certainly was to the Controller and Sir Michael Cary, the latter hired a nearby conference centre and brought the main elements of the differing tribes and the Turner working party together for a weekend of discussion. Mr Turner, as chairman of the working party, decided that he and Mr Fitzer (the DDEE) would, together, enunciate the majority functionalisation proposals and, as I had just been promoted to Rear-Admiral, they decided that I should try to explain the reasons behind the Forward Design and Resources Directorate which Sims found so abhorrent, before I scuttled off to America as naval attache. My presentation was later described by a senior civil servant as the most cogent condemnation of the Ship department ever given before the Board of Admiralty, but it contained little more than has already been explained in this account except chapter and verse as to why the lack of such a directorate was depriving the Director-General, and all of us in positions of responsibility, of an essential tool in the proper management of ship design. Perhaps its last paragraph will give the flavour.

> '*Let us recall that Mr Rowland Baker RCNC and one young Royal Canadian Navy constructor, followed by Mr Mason RCNC and Commander (E) E B Good RN and one Chinese gentleman were established on loan to Canada two years after the design process for the Whitby Class of frigates had commenced in the UK. In six years this small team designed the St Laurent Class, organised the Canadian shipyards, built the factories in Canada for marine machinery and finally commissioned the first ship 18 months ahead of the first of the Whitby class in the UK. That perhaps could be construed as a measure of our incompetence.*'

There was no meeting of minds whatever although Mr Sherwin, the director of naval construction (DNC), beloved and respected by all, came straight up to me at the conclusion of the conference and, handing me a large whisky and soda said, 'I don't agree with a word you said; but I liked the way you said it'.

Sir Michael Cary, who had been battling away for a year or more, would probably have imposed the working party's solution on Sir Alfred Sims. But Admiral Sir Horace Law, knowing that Sims' period as Director-General (ships) was drawing to a close, and not wishing to spoil what had been a tremendous surge forward in naval warship design and production by over-ruling him on a matter about which Sims felt so deeply, once again kicked the ball into touch. Another working party was proposed and this time was called a steering group. It consisted of Sims in the chair, the three directors and others as needed. The new director of marine engineering, Rear-Admiral Raper, although it was still not yet generally known, was to be the next Director-General (ships) and Law knew that Raper was a strong backer of the Turner working party recommendations.

The fundamental reorganisation of the whole warship design effort, made in response to a rapidly changing and increasingly complex technological and strategic situation with a politically inspired drastic reduction in civil service numbers, bedevilled by price inflation of defence equipment over and above national inflation, had to wait another ten years. Meanwhile, under Vice Admiral Sir George Raper and his successors, Mr Jack Daniels RCNC and Vice Admiral Sir Ted Horlick, the management and organisation of warship design made great strides on the functional lines recommended by Urwick Orr; and a much closer liaison with the naval staff and those in the secretariat holding the purse strings evolved, as the majority of the Turner working party had suggested.

Between the mid 1950s and the late 1970s, and despite many difficulties of organisation and overall naval design philosophy, a fleet was conceived, designed and built with formidable new weapon systems and possessing a mobility that enabled it, without any warning or preparation to show the world a few years later the realities of the reach of maritime power. These realities were founded on the twin Fisher concepts of up to date technology applied to the fleet by an officer corps of different professional disciplines, all of them with some community of knowledge and a lifelong community of sentiment, just as Fisher had wished.

That the changes in organisation of warship design and most notably in the new officer structure bringing engineers into the main stream of naval responsibility, still not yet fully complete and not yet perfect, were of inestimable benefit to those at the 'sharp end' can be deduced from the views of the Captain of HMS *Invincible* (Captain J J Black DSO, now Admiral Sir Jeremy Black, KCB,DSO,MBE), expressed to the Fellowship of Engineering early in 1983.

> '*The most striking features of* Invincible'*s performance whilst we were away were redundancy, maintainability and reliability; importantly reliability and here the design authorities and the quality assurance world should take due credit. We were at sea and operating for five and a half months without pause...On the way back (from the Falklands), just two days out from the UK, we conducted a full power trial and, even after all that time and all that usage, the readings came up precisely as we would have wished, and I think that is*

really remarkable.We are propelled by 4 Olympus gas turbine engines which give a wonderful flexibility; indeed they give the flexibility to be able to change an engine (from the spares we carry) and this we did on two separate occasions and during that time I still had some 85% of full speed available to me. This is ample for most operations so that here we have a flexibility totally unknown hitherto...Reliability was also manifest in the Weapon Electrical department., notably in the weapon systems and in command and control: and here it enabled me to conduct the anti-air warfare co-ordination for the entire force throughout the whole campaign. Indeed not only throughout the fighting but throughout the time we were down there we were the anti-air warfare control ship...'

In the 1980s, to carry the process of change beyond the Falklands, in order to match a changing world and in a naval climate where engineering was at last being recognised as a vital feature of naval life, Admiral Sir Lindsay Bryson GCB, later President of the Institution of Electrical Engineers and Lord Lieutenant of East Sussex, a weapon engineer of great wisdom and drive, became the first engineering specialist to be Controller of the Navy. Bryson wrought his improvements on the foundations conceived in the Fisher tradition by Admiral Sir Patrick Brind and The Hon Ewen Montague KC in the immediate aftermath of World War II (*chapter 11*). But the ensuing building work by Admirals Ford, Lewin, Mason, Mansergh, Middleton, Noble, Peard, by Lords Murray and Geddes, Vice Admiral Horlick, Mr Justice Nihill, Vice Admiral Raper and particularly by Admirals Reid as Third Sea Lord and Controller and The Hon Guy Russell as Second Sea Lord and Chief of Naval Personnel and later Admiral Sir Charles Madden,Bart, Sir Michael Cary, Sir Alfred Sims, Mr Turner *et al* had been proceeding steadily for over three decades. It should be emphasised too that all this activity had been spurred on by the many enlightened and war experienced Boards of Admiralty. Improvements in the management of warship design and in the influence which professional and sea experienced engineers can now exercise, if not emasculated by reorganisations, quick fixes or improvidence, will continue to give the fleet the fighting power, mobility and general serviceability that will enable it to cope with the even more terrible threats of the future.

Epilogue

Admiralty is the understanding of the uses of seapower. It must be fed from the blood and marrow of a people accustomed to the sea, but as an instrument it is shaped by skill and wisdom enduring and enlarged from generation to generation of seamen and statesmen who understand the sea. Skill, wisdom, understanding are kept alive only in the constant exercise of power at sea. A navy cannot be created on the occasion of crisis. A navy cannot be improvised. It must have continuity. The young hands learn from the old hands in the practice of their arts. Tradition embodies and preserves experience and knowledge from generation to generation. For both knowledge and the practice of the arts of Admiralty, the Royal Navy is the first of schools.

The Price of Admiralty
Paul and Margaret McGuire OUP Melbourne 1944

I bought *The Price of Admiralty* from Angus and Robertson's bookshop in Sydney in 1945. The story it told seemed, at first, besides imparting the tale of the late Captain Jefferson Hirst Walker MVO DSC RAN, one of Australia's great sea warriors of World War II, to state certain inalienable truths, but when my ship met the American fleet, then at the end of the greatest maritime campaign the world has known, I started to question whether the Royal Navy was still 'the first of schools'. Today I wonder too whether, in Britain, a generation of seamen and statesmen who understand the sea exists at all.

From Fisher to the Falklands has tried to give an account of the ups and downs and final ups of naval technology, particularly with regard to mobility, between the last years of the nineteenth century and the end of the 1960s, when I ceased to have any direct knowledge of naval engineering affairs, and when the decision to turn the Navy over to gas turbine propulsion, a twenty year programme, had been taken. During the previous twenty-five years, those who I have dubbed the 'revolutionaries', Baker, Dymoke, Hall, Harrison-Smith, Hawkins, Maclean, Norton, Raper, Ridley, Tracy, Trewby, Tyrrell, Walker, as well as many others of their generations, had started to improve the Navy's mobility by higher steam pressures and temperatures, high speed diesels, gas turbines, the better use of petroleum technology and, had government permitted, nuclear power. Gas turbines had won.

So dramatic a change, little different in magnitude from sail to steam, would never have been taken had it not been for Fisher's influence in the early part of the century on those newly joined officers of all specialisations who would come to the top of the tree forty years later, in the late 1940s and early 1950s. The 1950 move from a big ship to a small ship Navy made change essential, but it was those officers, some on the Board of Admiralty, some not, who finally repaired the mistakes of the 1920s and restored to the Navy, via the Mansergh (officer structure) committee, the influence of engineering on Naval affairs that, by 1939, the Navy had so tragically denied itself. In this context the far too long deferred birth of a uniformed electrical engineering branch with sea experience, today merged with mechanical engineers into a weapon engineering branch, has been crucially important. The lost years between 1924 and 1945 were lost forever, but, as HMS *Gloucester* showed in the Gulf, guns, missiles, sensors and communications have now reached the same degree of excellence both in attack and defence, in capability and serviceability under ocean going and battle conditions, as have the new propulsion systems in their contribution to that vital but often neglected weapon, mobility.

Having been forbidden by a short sighted British government to develop nuclear propulsion the Royal Navy was fortunate that the friendship with the United States Navy led to a special relationship, resting on mutual respect. For a time this was not so with the other services despite the friendliness which exists between the two air forces, but Montgomery and Bradley ensured that the armies at least for many years, would create no such bond as General de la Billiere seems now to have managed.

AF Lord Fraser of North Cape, as C in C Home Fleet, East Indies Fleet and then of the British Pacific Fleet, and Commander, later AF Sir Michael Le Fanu, as the British liaison officer with the US Pacific fleet, both confidants of those great US Admirals McCain, Halsey, Spruance, Arleigh Burke and Nimitz, were perhaps, with Mountbatten, when he was Chief of Combined Operations, the revivers of the special relationship between Admiral Jellicoe and Admiral Sims USN. Fleet Admiral King USN and A B Cunningham, Britain's great fighting admiral, each mistrusting the other, still managed to work together. Chiefs of Naval Operations such as Gerauld Wright and Anderson and that great aviator Admiral Thomas H Moorer USN and his more recent successors, Chiefs of Bureau of Ships including Admiral Mumma USN and Admiral Galantin USN, all the many Supreme Allied Commanders, Atlantic, and a veritable host of their subordinates have followed the same cooperative path. Meanwhile British Admirals such as Noble, Little, Somerville, Denny, Nigel Henderson and others kept the flame of mutual respect burning brightly in Washington DC.

Politicians and, with more reason, diplomats, often preen themselves on Britain's relationships with the United States, but between the Churchill/Roosevelt partnership and the Reagan/Thatcher entente it was the two navies, backed for some of the time by the intelligence community, that kept the special relationship alive and flourishing. This was maintained despite occasional intense political mistrust between leaders of the two nations.

US goodwill, and even some respect for our older but far smaller Navy, permitted us to glean the secrets and expertise of submarine nuclear propulsion, despite Admiral Rickover's reservations which had to be overruled. HMS *Dreadnought*'s launch on Trafalgar Day 1960 was a landmark in British Naval history, leading as it did to the possibility of a Polaris fleet. With the help of Admiral Levering-Smith KBE (Hon) USN, the father of the Polaris missile, that priceless possession has prevented us being blackmailed. Our fleet of highly sophisticated nuclear propelled hunter-killer submarines contribute significantly to the maintenance of the Atlantic bridge. The world leadership by the Royal Navy in the development of marine gas turbine propulsion and the highly innovative British Harrier aircraft much used by the US Marine Corps, the deck landing sight and the steam catapult, are all worthwhile returns from the RN to the USN and to the US Coast Guard, the third largest navy in the world.

The growing towards each other of the three British services, of which the Navy is by far the smallest (and therefore its needs the most apt to be disregarded), has much to commend it. Like any major change this growing together has a heavy price, in this case in three areas: a paper blizzard; a proliferating bureaucracy and uncertain political direction. So many in positions of power seem unable to comprehend the critical strategic complexities facing an island nation situated on the ocean flank of Europe, yet still possessing wide international influence thanks to our past, our diplomats and our national reputation, so greatly enhanced since the Falklands and by the Gulf war.

I served for ten years in the old Admiralty with its quirky ways, its triumphs of the building of a Polaris fleet to time and within the original estimate and the move back to the Fisher concept of a General List of officers, and occasional disastrous blunders (the large carrier affair). For my last five years I presided over the Defence Intelligence Staff (DIS), the then only true tri-service/civilian organisation. The paper blizzard is often the result of inter-service good will (no-one conceivably must be forgotten) and the economics of common weapon development; thus a burgeoning bureaucracy armed with copying machines is created and security suffers.

Today, as the Soviet empire tries to cope as Britain once coped with the dissolution of empire, future strategy and the size and shape of Britain's armed forces present the UK and its allies with problems for which there can be no quick fixes. Throughout Russia's history, as one regime has cast out another, she has invariably returned to authoritarian or totalitarian rule. It is as if one vertebra is missing from Mother Russia's backbone. There is a lesson here that the West neglects at its peril.

The three great economic entities in the next half century seem likely to be Japan (possibly with China), America and a Europe extending perhaps eventually to the Urals. Beyond all doubt the 200 per minute net increase in the world's population will reinforce nationalism, lead to further and possibly irreversible environmental pollution and, with the unstinting help of television, stoke the embers of conflict, world wide terrorism and, probably, all out war in the Middle East.

As defence technology becomes more complicated and expensive and as elected politicians and civil servants find difficulty in maintaining such technical literacy as they may have acquired, so the top level geopolitical-military decision making process becomes more of a sweepstake. In Britain the same antipathy to engineers that caused the Navy to abrogate Fisher's reforms in the 1920s still permeates parliament and society in general. Since the demise of the uniquely talented Royal Naval Scientific Service (RNSS), with men like Sir John Carroll and Sir Basil Lythall, their predecessors at the top before my time, and countless others, so helpful to a Navy whose strategic and technological problems they well comprehended, there has been a change for the worse. Scientists, often from the quiet groves of academe, and not always very practical in their ideas on future naval warfare, have tended to exert a hypnotic effect on politicians and senior officials. As the Chairman of the House of Commons Defence Committee once remarked, as a civilian witness deployed his voluble rhetoric in the presence of a Naval co-witness, 'the silent service seems more than usually reticent today'. The views of sea experienced naval officers trained to deal with the perils and obstacles provided by the corrosive impact of sea and weather, and by the chaos and the unpredictable damage and the fog of maritime war are sometimes not put forward with the force they should be. This is a symptom of an over-worked Navy necessarily devoting whatever officer training time remains available to the professional training of a sea-warrior, and not a Whitehall warrior. It was my view, founded on 'drafting and sickness margins' offered me by the three services when re-vamping the Joint Services Staff College curriculum in 1970 that the Naval officer had less 'down-time', in the sense that he could never devote himself to anything other than purely professional betterment. Necessarily, the bigger the service the more flexibility in appointing (posting). The Navy, due to its size, comes off worst. This is an aspect the Manadon Board of Visitors cannot directly take into account, but the creation of an ability by Naval officers to articulate and argue logically is something for which the college might find room in the syllabus.

Professor F H Garner OBE in his famous Redwood Memorial Lecture in 1951 and the great Lord Willis Jackson, FRS, a decade later, warned against those with no knowledge of engineering being taken in by well presented scientific dreams. This is a particular problem in a minimum manpower Navy, increasingly dependent for its fighting effectiveness on advanced technology, certainly to a far greater extent than the other services. It is not true that the Navy is 'agin' scientists. The Navy has always welcomed scientists who understand the particular perils of sea warfare over, on or under the ocean. Their wisdom and experience has been beyond price to professional naval engineers who have to judge and advise on what is progress and what is not.

The many forward-looking Boards of Admiralty since 1945 have stressed the need for all Naval officers to be technically minded, and also for the officer corps to contain a proportion of Navally trained professional and sea experienced marine, weapon and air engineers. With the lessons of World War II very much alive in their minds, the post-war Boards discarded their predecessors' contempt for 'engineers' and built a great technical university for the Navy, the Royal Naval Engineering College, to which eventually most officers would go for long or short periods, depending on their role in war and their specialisation. In taking this far sighted step they realised the truth their forbears forgot when they saw an engineer in oil spattered overalls. In the words of Cicero, '*Saepe est sub pallio sordido sapientia*' (wisdom is often found under a shabby cloak).

As I described in *The Man Around the Engine*, to spend years at one's most impressionable age with other young men, confined in a hot humid steel box, surrounded by coloured pipes full of different sorts of high pressure superheated steam, driving machines at several thousand revolutions a minute, with the constant scream of fans making normal conversation impossible, listening to guns firing and bombs exploding, is an experience, terrifying at the time though it was, I am now glad I did not miss. Holding their hands and listening to their whispers as they died from dreadful wounds, or swimming in a rough sea with the same sort of men in the blackness of the night as one's ship slips beneath the waves, made me realise that an extraordinary reservoir of spirit existed in the pre-war Navy, despite Invergordon; especially perhaps in the Mediterranean Fleet under Admiral Sir William Fisher. The Rev Tubby Clayton of Toc H fame once described the Mediterranean Fleet as 'a city of silver grey with its good humoured citizens'. There was a sense of wonderment too, as to how that spirit was transmitted and made to pervade the multitude of young 'hostilities only' sailors, seasick, homesick, and conscripted into the battle line of the wartime Navy across the oceans of the world.

Today the Royal Navy still seems to attract a breed of youngsters who, even in the too short time permitted for training ashore, are the strength of the Navy while serving and of the community when they leave.

I was fortunate not only to be associated with Admiral Mansergh's committee, which brought engineering into the main stream of Naval life, but also to be staff officer and co-secretary to Lord Murray's committee which elevated the naval academic entry standard and put the seal on naval training for deck and engineer officers of the future, by their recommendation that officers of all

A new Naval recruit, on joining and after 6 and 12 weeks of training (photographs author's collection).

specialisations should go to the Royal Naval Engineering College at Manadon for their academic training. Working with the Murray committee I came to learn, from the wisdom of the four civilian committee members, how in the hearts of Englishmen the Navy occupies the position reserved in the pre-war Germany for their army. The committee proposed that an officer's early training should be very different and more austere and harder than the rather slack and untraditional regime which had mistakenly been allowed to prevail.

The committee also believed that the influence of technology in all its naval applications keeps the Navy from going to seed in time of peace, which can happen in all three services due to pressures for military economy. They were insistent that the ardent young men at Dartmouth and in the Training Squadron must be prepared through their training, both spiritually and intellectually, to accept a life at sea in many ways harder than that of their contemporaries ashore; and also to accept in this age of galloping technology a degree of engineering training appropriate to their naval duties at the naval technical university at Manadon to which the committee hoped all officers would go.

Especially interesting to me, with my engineering background, is the tough technological education and training given in three hectic years of 42 weeks each, to the varieties of engineering officer entered from a wide swathe of civilian and Naval society (the latter providing 40% from the lower deck through the apprentice entry), altogether now totalling a third of the Navy's officer strength, reading for their Bachelor and Master of Engineering degrees; as well as those seamen and supply officers reading for a Bachelor of Arts degree in maritime defence technology and management, 'all of one company', as the late Admiral Sir Aubrey Mansergh so hoped they would become. This they are becoming at the RN Engineering College. The Naval officers under training and a sizeable number of WRNS, and officers from the other services and foreign and commonwealth navies, are inheriting the legacy left by those who knew of Admiral Lord Fisher and his vision for the Royal Navy. The legacy too of those who either laid the foundations in the 1940s for the present effective fleet or built on those foundations so fruitfully throughout the last four decades.

Equally importantly, Manadon is a disciplined Naval general training establishment, where future officers are led to discover themselves. When they leave they possess professional and, some of them, highly professional, skills. They are also endowed with the seeds of loyalty, tradition, courage, hardihood and of pride in the Navy; and with a determination to do their duty, not only in the better future design of highly mobile, well armed ocean going warships and aircraft, but also at sea or in battle when tired, sick, frightened or alone, to the uttermost limit of their capacity.The test of leadership is still to be able to inspire others with those qualities. Fortitude has been defined as grace under pressure. In battle, as in the topsy-turvy world we live in, the measure of an officer's success as a leader is the spread of fortitude; of his failure despair. I have seen both.

In 1982, just forty years after the mobility revolution started, a new Royal Navy was well equipped, trained and instantly ready for a war into which it was plunged with no prior warning. On the Monday after the invasion of the Falklands on the previous Friday, a fleet, each ship equipped to take on board fuel and stores while under way (as Fisher had recommended 70 years before and as the RN, having forgotten Fisher, had learnt from the USN 35 years before), started to leave English shores; similarly equipped ships, after many weeks at sea on exercises, also moved towards the South Atlantic. A nuclear hunter-killer submarine capable of high underwater speed was also on the way. She was followed on the Monday and following days by two aircraft carriers with 30 Sea Harriers and 33 Sea King helicopters, two assault ships, twenty or more frigates, four more submarines, a very adequate fleet train from the Royal Fleet Auxiliary and taken up from trade together with nine troop ships converted from cruise liners. In the end well over 100 ships and 170 aircraft and their crews had to be kept fed, fuelled, stored, ammunitioned and maintained serviceable in the face of whatever the oceans or the enemy could throw at them.

Much has rightly been made of the bravery, initiative and endurance of the men and ships that went to the Falklands, but that they got there at all, that they carried on the war for so long and in such conditions, was the result of the adoption by the post World War II Boards of Admiralty, starting with that of Admiral of the Fleet Lord Fraser, of the philosophy that a navy must be completely mobile and able to operate on its own across the oceans of the world; and of the detailed planning by generations of naval officers and civil servants that that concept entailed. If, as Nelson's fleet could do, today's ships could not stay at sea and self supporting for two years or so, then at least they must improve on Lord Fraser's estimate to Nimitz of eight days' front line operation. The Falklands showed that they could, with the help of ships from trade and their brave civilian crews. That was not all. The ships of the fleet were commanded by 'captains of war' trained in all aspects and limitations of their highly sophisticated weapons and machinery, and how best and with what tactics these could be used against the enemy. With them into battle went their engineers, trained to maintain, in the face of a very hostile ocean environment and enemy action, their ship's war fighting capability; a capability towards which, with recognisable professional and sea experienced authority, they or their engineering seniors had already guided the designers of both the weapons and machinery now deployed in their charge against the enemy. Both captains and engineers were motivated by 'some community of knowledge and a lifelong community of sentiment'. There was now no longer that divisiveness between those above decks and those below by which, especially since the coming of steam but even before, the Navy had for so long been bedevilled. Both sorts of officer were 'as of one company'.

Happily for the outcome of the battle, the Navy also still enjoyed that unique special relationship in the shape of Caspar Weinberger, the Pentagon's staunch anglophile Secretary for Defence. That was why the weapons a penny pinching era in British economic history denied the Navy, were sent by the United States.

As a weapon of war for the statesman to wield in 1982 the Navy was already fully mobile with experienced leaders and with propulsion machinery and a Royal Fleet Auxiliary fleet train and a 'ghost fleet train' to be taken up from trade that gave it immense reach. With the two main exceptions, short range anti-missile weapons and over the horizon radar, it was also just, but only just, otherwise adequately armed. The result was the ability to plan a campaign and put ashore a brigade of Royal Marines reinforced with two parachute battalions, associated artillery, light tanks and army air corps and Naval helicopters, and then a second brigade of soldiers; and sustain the battle at sea, ashore and in the air, with inevitable casualties of men and ships and aircraft, for three months, 8000 miles from base, in winter, in the roughest ocean in the world. This could never have been accomplished forty years before.

It was a close run thing. Had it not been for the moral courage of two successive great First Sea Lords, backed politically throughout the years before by a predecessor then in the House of Lords, Argentina would hold the Falklands today. By his action in 1982, the then incumbent First Sea Lord, Admiral of the Fleet Sir Henry Leach, with total trust in the men and mechanisms of the fleet confided to his care by Admiral of the Fleet Lord Lewin, by then Chief of Defence Staff, saved the government from falling, restored to Britain her faith in herself and set in motion a change in the national and international climate which still continues. But the lack of understanding by land minded politicians and dreamy scientists of the need for a Navy has not yet greatly diminished. As a country, for every unit (joule) of home produced food energy eaten, ten energy units (joules) of fossil fuel must be imported by sea in order to grow it, in addition to all the raw materials for manufacturers, by whose efforts the economy and so society tries to survive.

Tragically, despite the British Maritime League, the Greenwich Forum, the Parliamentary maritime group, all working under the scourge of Commander Michael Ranken a well known Naval engineer, as well as the very perceptive Select Committee on Defence, the British Chamber of Shipping and the Institute of Marine Engineers, those who man our merchant ships (to whose predecessors, at a cost of 30,000 casualties, we owed our wartime survival), have almost disappeared; and the number of fisherfolk is on the same disastrous downward trend. Statesmen and their civil servants, hopping frantically from airport to airport, altogether lack a sea-sense.

At the beginning of this epilogue I questioned whether the UK is now a maritime nation. I am sure that the instinct still abounds but I am also sure that it is being fast diluted. It seems to be fading amongst the young due to a lack of any truthful education in the nation's maritime heritage. I can detect no feeling amongst the nation's leaders for a future which, European community or not, will always depend on the oceans.

From the days of discovery and colonisation Britain has looked to the sea. In times of peril the sea has been an ally, and in times of peace, a source of prosperity. Sometimes hostile, sometimes generous, the oceans have always offered their abundant resources, but, in a time of mounting economic needs and of congested populations, concern for the sea has rapidly begun to fade. How fully and wisely the sea is used in the years ahead will profoundly affect the supply of cheap raw materials and the increasing demands for food. Inevitably, as an island, there is a need for a manpower economic, high technology Royal Navy, whereby the security for such as pass on the seas upon their lawful occasions can be guaranteed, because wherever there is wealth, as there is on the sea-bed, there will be conflict.

As the Statement on Defence said thirty years ago, 'The ability to assure free movement by sea at the right time and place remains of fundamental importance to these islands; indeed the sea may in certain circumstances be the one open highway for strategic movement free of international political hindrance'. The Falklands story and the clearance of mines from the Gulf will not spell the last triumphs of the Royal Navy so long as statesmen recall the world's history.

To preserve the Atlantic bridge, to sustain the special relationship in the face of the political and military and ideological hurricanes of the future is as vital to the European community, indeed to the world community, as to the UK. Nonetheless, since the Falklands, the merchant fleet has almost disappeared, while fisheries are disregarded and the shipbuilding industry, wrenched by Harold Macmillan from its effective sponsorship by the Admiralty and divorced of any subsidy, has been allowed to wither away. As a nation, as the island on the ocean flank of the European Community, indissolubly linked across the sea with the greatest and most benign influence on the future of mankind, we seem either afraid or no longer willing to pay the price of Admiralty.

Appendix

Memorandum by the Engineer in Chief of the Fleet
on giving up office in September 1957

FIRST SEA LORD
(Copy to: Second Sea Lord, Controller of the Navy)

VALEDICTORY

1. On relinquishing the post of Engineer in Chief of the Fleet, I feel I should put on paper my thoughts about the position at which we have now arrived as the result of AFO 1/56 and my hopes and fears for the future.

2. I believe that in adopting the principles set out in AFO 1/56 the Navy did a great thing. The Board of our day, faced with a similar situation to that which faced the Board of Lord Beatty, took exactly the opposite step; it decided for integration as distinct from segregation. It was not that Lord Beatty and his Board did not fully appreciate the situation; that they did so is shown by a Minute (attached herewith as an addendum) dated 1920 signed by Lord Beatty, a copy of which I have found amongst office papers. Much of this Minute is very significant, as will be seen.

3. In doing what has been done I believe the Navy has put itself to the test and the results are being closely watched both from within and without. Necessarily results will be slow in coming and spectacular ones are not to be looked for, if only because the Queen's business must go on; there must be a smooth transition from a Navy of officers trained in a Branch tradition to a one officered from a General List of common origin and purpose. This transition will take at least a generation to effect, and at any time during this period reaction could destroy the intentions of AFO 1/56.

4. One of the underlying reasons why the Mansergh Committee was set up was the clear evidence that the Engineering Branch was running down. Often, before the Committee was set up, I

posed the question to the Sea Lords and other senior Naval Officers: Do you think that an efficient Engineering Branch is necessary for the well being of the Navy ? If the answer is 'No', you need do nothing for it is dying on its feet; if 'Yes', something must be done very quickly and I suggest along the lines of the Selborne-Fisher scheme.

5.   One thing is certain; the hopes of Engineering Officers in common with all non-Seaman Officers have been raised by AFO 1/56, for in it they see the opportunity of advancing beyond the secondary and advisory role which they have hitherto filled, to positions of authority in which they can take individual responsibility for their own decisions and share in the collective decisions of the Board of Admiralty. If these hopes are not fulfilled, the former trend will be resumed with added impetus. In my view Engineering in the Navy would then finally wither and soon die as an effective component of the Officer Corps.

6.   I see a number of dangers close at hand which can stultify the high intentions of AFO 1/56. The fact that they spring from perfectly natural causes makes them none the less dangerous; the more so as the motives which give rise to them are sincere.

7.   The primary danger is an understandable reluctance of the late Executive Branch to share their hitherto sole authority with other sorts of Naval Officer. If this were to prevail I am quite certain in my own mind that it is the Navy which will suffer eclipse and not merely the Engineering specialisation, for I do not believe the Navy can survive without a large and healthy component which is thoroughly versed in the technology of its day and age. To be so versed spells recognised professional status, for nothing less will provide the essential foundations of knowledge.

8.   I am disturbed by the reluctance which I detect to recognise this, unpalatable as it must be to anyone brought up to believe that the Executive Branch was the Navy. I cannot rid myself of the feeling that this belief is widely held amongst the junior and middle ranks and even the lower senior ranks. Many have told me (and not just Engineering Officers) it was a clearly understood thing that if you wanted to take up engineering you were to all intents and purposes lost to the Navy. This can easily

be denied because it was never a conscious doctrine—it will take a great deal to put this into reverse, yet the sooner it is, the better. I believe there is even a school of thought which holds that the Navy can be run without any technical officers of professional standing; that is to say it could be run by Special Duties List technicians and skilled ratings, with its equipment provided by professional Civil Servants. That ships could be run like this is unquestionable, but what sort of ships would they be ? This attitude of mind has been fostered by a lack of proper understanding at Dartmouth of the place of technology in Naval affairs.

9.   Another danger is that administrative difficulties may be allowed to block the promotion of non-seamen into the higher ranks and their appointment to positions of wider influence and authority. It would be quite easy to produce a host of reasons why the scales should be tipped (two examples are the opposition of professional Civil Servants and the need to find employment for seamen on the Flag List in order to avoid too swift a fall in their numbers and promotion prospects and the way has been made almost fatally tempting and clear by the extent to which the safeguards built into AFO 1/56 have already been whittled away.) In particular the protection afforded by the split Flag List has been removed, with the result that the Post List can flood across into jobs previously reserved for the General List, thus setting at nought the intention of the Mansergh Committee. A common Flag List is of course a proper and inevitable objective, but I feel sure in its early years the new and untried General List conception needed the protection from predatory incursions which has now been removed. This alone can quite easily be fatal to AFO 1/56 and, in my judgement, the Navy. The Post List is not and cannot ever be self sufficing and self sustaining.

10.   Perhaps I ought to explain what I mean by 'administrative difficulties'. The danger I have referred to in para 9 could arise simply from lack of forward planning; getting the right man into the right place at the right time. Only a deliberate plan can ensure this and, however much it may have to be altered, such a plan is essential if a due proportion of 'bright' people is to appear in each batch. It is not too early to start looking for possible top candidates when they are quite young, say with a

few years in as a Commander. For some time to come it will be necessary for the Engineer in Chief to be closely associated with this planning; more closely indeed than I am at the moment.

11. I have also detected what, to me, is a curious refusal to admit even today that there are non-seamen officers who can also be essentially naval and capable of adapting themselves readily to situations not previously within their immediate experience. I should have thought that their record in command of shore establishments, now some ten years old, would have dispelled any such doubts ,but it clearly has not done so and this sharpens the danger because the upward movement of non-seamen officers may be delayed to such an extent that the good intentions of AFO 1/56 will be lost. This would be equally disastrous.

12. I am fully alive to the fact that the sentiments which I have attributed to the late Executive Branch do not derive from plain arrogance. The history of inter Branch relationships during my own naval career has taught me that the Engineering Branch is no less to blame with its tendency to 'class consciousness' and declared self-sufficiency. Disdain has been met by disdain and the only thing to suffer has been the Navy. Nevertheless the cause of 'class consciousness', however far back it may be, is under-privilege. There are some incidents in my own career of which I am ashamed, and I determined long ago that such things should not recur if it lay in my power to prevent them.

13. These troubles I ascribe in the main to the entirely separate methods of entry in the latter part of the 19th century and the years before the first war, the influence of which has been felt down to very recent years. In my view, the only reasonable cure is likely to be common entry and identical training carried on for as long as possible and certainly throughout the whole period at Dartmouth. Even now very little is being done to ensure that Seaman Officers really understand the true role of the Engineer although much interest is rightly laid on introducing Engineer Officers to the role of the Seaman.

14. In the past Executive Officers by and large have taken little interest in the power plants of their ships in contrast to the armament in which, by the nature of things, they often had to interest themselves closely. The good ones and I have served

with many, paid us the compliment of assuming that it did not need their attention although for morale purposes I would have welcomed it. The not so good simply did not bother as long as all went well, but lacked sympathy and understanding when it didn't. On the other hand many Engineering Officers have made it difficult for their Captains and others by guarding their preserves with a narrow zeal.

15. I should not like anything I have said to cause it to be believed that I have lost faith in AFO 1/56 or the Navy. I assuredly have not, but in my considered opinion their fates are indissolubly joined.

16. It would be a pity if the Navy went down in frustration and eclipse just when it seems likely that it will emerge as the only Service which really counts in local, limited, global and even broken backed wars. Open sea lanes can alone ensure that free flow of international trade needed to sustain civilised existence. This unimpeded flow seems to me to be a necessary condition if we are not to relapse into that barbarism which is not so far beneath the surface of modern industrial civilisation. Navies seem to me to be the best guarantee that this condition is fulfilled and so the role of our Navy is still its traditional one; to keep open the sea lanes and to take striking power where it can do most harm to the enemy. There seem to be many influences at work to destroy the Navy; it behoves us to see we do not destroy ourselves as the result of an internal struggle for power, always one of the besetting sins of mankind.

17. I consider therefore that during the period of conversion to the General List, which will last certainly for a generation and probably longer, the situation will need unremitting vigilance by successive Boards of Admiralty, if only because men by nature prefer to do the things that coincide with their immediate personal interests rather than 'to perceive and know what things they ought to do'.

18. In thus opening out my heart to you I am aware with deep thankfulness that in a number of places, notably in Her Majesty's Ships, the tide is now on the make. My fear is that the growing recognition and identity of purpose and brotherhood may be strangled almost as soon as it is born. This situation

could arise almost imperceptibly if the many and conflicting pressures on the centre were to cause wise direction and strength of purpose to falter.

F.T. MASON
ENGINEER IN CHIEF OF THE FLEET
20.9.57

Addendum to Appendix

Memorandum by First Sea Lord on CE 7887/20 (ADM1/6/20)
leading to Board decision on E-in-C's responsibilities as
Engineer in Chief of the Navy as promulgated in Office Memo
No 149/20 of 1.6.20.

FUTURE OF THE ENGINEERING BRANCH

1. The Naval Policy statement to Parliament laid down definitely the separation of the Engineering Branch on the one side from the Deck Branch on the other, and it foreshadowed the opening up to Engineer Officers of important higher administrative positions which would make the Engineering side an equal career in every respect to the Deck side, and would therefore attract a proportion of the best brains of the Service.

2. It is desirable that steps should be taken as rapidly as possible to give this idea concrete expression; although at the moment we may obtain sufficient volunteers, owing to the fact that we have amongst Sub-Lieutenants and Midshipmen a surplus, this surplus will soon be expended, and unless we are able to make the prospects of the Engineering Branch really good the volunteers for it will fall in numbers and also in intellectual standard.

3. The need of a clear policy with regard to Engineering is also evident as judged by the opinions of many of the younger Engineer Officers,who see in the Admiralty announcements made during the War and since the War a curtailment of chances of openings on the Engineering side of the profession. This discontent on their part must be swept away, otherwise the bad effect on recruiting for the branch is bound to be bad.

4. A survey of the Engineering side shows that whereas in the junior positions the conditions of service approximate to those of Specialist Officers in the Deck Branch, that as regards higher positions, there are far fewer of them, and those there are do not carry emoluments equal to those enjoyed by Deck Officers in analagous positions. Any scheme therefore which contemplates raising the prospects for Engineering Officers, at the same time conforming to the principles laid down in the

Naval Policy statement and increasing general efficiency, must commence from the top, and must in fact commence with the office of the Engineer in Chief of the Navy.

5. The present duties of the Engineer in Chief are laid down in the Admiralty pamphlet on the Duties of the Controller. It appears from these duties that the holder of such an office, in charge of the whole field of Engineering—policy, design, administration and supply—is overloaded with detail. As a consequence, design and supply assume a greater importance than policy, and the staff side of Engineering suffers accordingly.

6. To increase efficiency it is considered that the lines on which the Naval staff side developed should be followed, and that the office of the Engineer in Chief should be separated into three divisions:-

    (a) the Staff side, with the Engineer in Chief at its head, and with sections under him dealing with Engineering policy, principles of Engineering training and lines of Engineering development.

    (b) the Personnel side, dealing with the administration and provision of Engineering personnel.

    (c) the Design side, dealing with design and supply to meet requirements of Engineering policy.

7. The Staff side of Engineering would be linked up with the Deck Branch and the Board of Admiralty through the Chief of the Naval Staff; the Personnel side through the Second Sea Lord; and the Design side through the Controller, and thus the Engineering Branch would become similar in its higher organisation to the Deck Branch. Similar positions would be open and there would be additional avenues fro promotion.

8. Further, as a result of this higher organisation, changes will gradually be made in the Engineering position in Dockyards and sea commands. It is premature, however, to consider these matters until the first change at the Admiralty has been made, the definite lines of the future Engineering policy established, and until we see more clearly what are the requirements.

(Sgd) Beatty
8.4.20.

Acknowledgments

In composing *From Fisher to the Falklands,* which has become two books, *The Man Around the Engine* (Kenneth Mason) and this book, I have received much help. My interest in Fisher and his ideas was triggered by Michael Lewis when he taught me at Dartmouth well before his famous Professorship at the Royal Naval College, Greenwich from which successive generations of naval officers have so greatly benefited.

I have drawn extensively from Winston Churchill's *World Crisis* and *Second World War,* from Lord Fisher's own memoranda in the Admiralty Library and my own copy of his *Memories,* from Professor Ruddock Mackay's exceptionally helpful *Fisher,* and from various documents in the Public Record Office whose staff have always given me such willing help which I gratefully acknowledge. Admiral of the Fleet Lord Chatfield's *The Navy and Defence* proved a mine of information as did Admiral Sir William James' *Life of Sir William Fisher.* Admiral Bacon's lives of *Fisher* and *Jellicoe* have both provided much background, as have Admiral Sir Herbert Richmond's *Statesmen and Seapower,* Richard Humble's *Fraser of North Cape,* Viscount Cunningham's *A Sailor's Odyssey* and the many books published about the recapture of the Falklands and South Georgia in 1982.

It was Captain Stephen Roskill who encouraged me to write of engineers and engineering and his books *British Naval Policy between the Wars* and *The Royal Navy at War* have proved invaluable. But I doubt whether I would have ever started if David Divine, that brave war correspondent of the *Sunday Times,* had not given me his friendship and had not constantly harried me to get on with it. If he was still with us which to my regret he no longer is, I hope he would not be too disappointed with the results.

It has always been a sadness to me that Professor Marder, that great American historian whose several books on Fisher I cherish and have constantly consulted, should have become a visiting Fellow at All Souls just as I became Naval Attache in Washington DC. And after some time we again crossed the Atlantic in opposite directions. So we never met. At his request I lent him most of the papers and reports I had amassed in the Pacific. Alas I kept no copies and he died just as they reached him; they have proved irrecoverable. Professor Potter's *Nimitz* provided me with the background to that historic maritime campaign by the US navy, of which I personally saw only the last few weeks. Admiral Elder USN of the US Naval Institute added much to knowledge and admiration for that extraordinary saga of the Pacific, as did Admiral Thomas H Moorer, Chief of Naval Operations and Admiral Jack McCain USN when he was CINCPAC.

Conversations with the late Vice Admiral (E) Sir Denys Ford and Vice Admiral Sir Frank Mason gave me an insight into how well the need for more professionally trained engineers was widely recognised after 1945, while the late Vice Admiral Sir George Raper corrected that part of the text of which he had personal knowledge. Commander Kit Hall and (from New Zealand) Commander Leonard Baker have added greatly to the story of what went on at Bath and at E in C's out stations as the 'engineering revolution' gathered pace. To them and to many other engineering and seamen officers some of whom I have named, I owe a great deal. If the book could have been longer there would have been many others to add to those I mention.

My debt to the Director of Public Relations (Navy) has again increased as has that I owe to Paul Kemp and his colleagues in the photographic department of the Imperial War Museum. Lieutenant-Commander John Maber has produced just what I wanted from his collection of ships' photos and to him and to Vickers, Yarrows, YARD and British Aerospace I record my thanks. Thanks are also due to Commander T R Shaw, Editor of the Journal of Naval Engineering for his help and to Mr Tony Davis of the Ministry of Defence.

Finally, it was Jolyon Sloggett, Secretary and mainspring of the Institute of Marine Engineers, of which I have been a member for nearly half a century, who offered to publish *From Fisher to the Falklands*. The hard work has fallen on David Long, the Technical Secretary, and Kate Williams, the editor, who has had to cope not only with my muddled use of a word processor, but also my eccentric punctuation. Without their good natured help this book would not have seen the light of day.